ART GLASS HANDBOOK

WITH PRICES

Revised 4th Edition

by

JOHN F. HOTCHKISS

ONE HUNDRED & FIFTY TYPES OF ART GLASS ARE DESCRIBED, AND ILLUSTRATED, MANY IN COLOR.

TWO THOUSAND PRICES FOR ALL KINDS, SIZES, SHAPES AND COLORS OF ART GLASS.

OVER FOUR HUNDRED PRICES ARE CROSS REFERENCED TO LARGE COLOR PICTURES IN *ART GLASS NOUVEAU* BY THE GROVERS.

ADVICE ON REPRODUCTIONS, COLOR, GLASS TERMS, MARKS, SIGNATURES AND IMPERFECTIONS.

HAWTHORN BOOKS, INC.
PUBLISHERS / *New York*

ART GLASS HANDBOOK WITH PRICES

Copyright © 1972 by John Hotchkiss. Copyright under International and Pan-American Copyright Conventions. All rights reserved, including the right to reproduce this book or portions thereof in any form, except for the inclusion of brief quotations in a review. All inquiries should be addressed to Hawthorn Books, Inc., 260 Madison Avenue, New York, New York 10016. This book was manufactured in the United States of America and published simultaneously in Canada by Prentice-Hall of Canada, Limited, 1870 Birchmount Road, Scarborough, Ontario. Library of Congress Catalog Card Number: 72-89769.

2 3 4 5 6 7 8 9 10

ACKNOWLEDGMENTS

The continued cooperation of many well informed persons has again made possible the up-dating and expansion of previous information on Art Glass prices. The ranks of these valuable assistants seem to grow with each new effort. Since some prefer to remain anonymous we have omitted any references to names, but to each and every one of them our heartfelt thanks.

This time we especially want to recognize the hundreds of unsolicited comments from readers of our other publications. If the information in here is more meaningful, useful, accurate, and better organized, it is due to their generosity in making suggestions. We still welcome the same sincere comments (good or bad) to keep us in tune with how to best serve the requirements of those interested in fine glass.

While we have found it impractical to list all those in the above two groups that have actively helped us, we certainly would be remiss if we did not publicly recognize the important contributions made by those auctioneers who have supplied pictures and prices from important auctions they have recently conducted. Early Auction Company, 232 Laurel Ave., Milford, Ohio; Parke-Bernet Galleries, Inc., 980 Madison Avenue, New York, N. Y.; Pennypacker Auction Centre, 1540 New Holland Road, Kenhorst, Reading, Pennsylvania; Bob, Chuck, & Rich Roan, Inc., RD 2, Coogan Station, Pennsylvania.

We are indebted to the following for the use of material :
Charles E. Tuttle Company
Corning Museum of Glass
Crown Publishers, Inc.
Forward Color Productions
Robert E. Rockwell
Sothebys/Parke-Bernet Galleries
Thomas Nelson & Sons
Harry H. Whitlow

TO FIDELIS

My wife who has maintained her equanimity throughout the eruptions and interruptions incident to this and other productions.

FOREWORD

The purpose of this book is two-fold. The first is to provide a handy and inexpensive source of ready information, including values, to be carried in the pocket, purse, or automobile. While it is particularly valuable to the beginning collector in this respect, it should also assist both the advanced collector and others with a more casual interest.

Secondly, it provides the reader with usable values for many items that are illustrated in full color in several other reference books on Art Glass such as: Grovers' *Art Glass Nouveau;* Barret's *Collectors Handbook of American Art Glass;* Revi's two books, 19*th Century Glass"* and *American Art Nouveau Glass.* These figures were determined with the assistance of many people and publications. They represent what a similar item would probably sell for at a city Antique Show. As is evident later, the common items will follow the appraisals quite closely. The scarce and rare items could and will deviate from the assigned figures by significant percentages. In using the valuations for such pieces, particular attention should be given to the section entitled *How to Use Price Information.*

With only our small book, the beginner can obtain enough concise information to satisfy him in the early stages of his new hobby and guide him in initial acquisitions. As his appetite for more knowledge and background grows, he can move on to one or more of the other books, which will act as valuable basic references for him in future years. This price handbook (or later editions) will still act as a companion piece showing current values. Many collectors narrow their field of interests as they learn more about some categories such as Steuben, Galle or Cut Glass. In this event, much more detailed information is available in numerous books that are mentioned in the bibliography and reference lists in the back.

For the dealer, appraiser, and owners of a few pieces, this book offers an ideal solution to their need for a brief information on identification and values and will satisfy this with a minimum of time, effort, and expense. For the person that has the responsibility of disposing of one or more articles, this manual should enlighten him on what he has and what he should ask in price. In some cases, it should clearly indicate to him that he has something of real merit and value, and should obtain additional help in the form of other books or an expert appraisal.

Acting either as a companion to one of the excellent reference books or as an independent source for identifying and pricing, this book has the potential of rendering valuable assistance in enlightened buying and selling of all types of art glass.

It is interesting to observe that in the last five years some types of very inexpensive recent machine made glass have far outstripped art glass in percentage of appreciation. These have reached the point where the present price of what was originally a mass produced reproduction is now selling for a price well above that of the original handmade one. This is particularly so with respect to Carnival Glass. The recent widespread interest in Depression Glass would lead one to conclude that the same thing could happen in this category. This might indicate that some of the earlier less expensive hand crafted pieces of Art Glass were still underpriced and that this gap would be closed. Cut Glass was in this same position and still is to a lesser extent.

INTRODUCTION

In assembling the latest information on Art Glass for this fourth edition we have endeavored to broaden the usefulness by adding abbreviated historical and related information on each classification. For a much more detailed account and additional illustrations all in full color a number of recommended books have been listed in the back of this one. We have leaned heavily on all of these books in the preparation of this pocket size manual. This smaller size has been adopted to give it more mobility than the larger size hard bound books. It has been made purse or pocket size to accompany you on your travels.

The material is presented by type or name of a particular glass in alphabetical order for quick reference. All the information on one type can be scanned in a few minutes. More than four hundred of the thousands of prices in this book are cross-referenced by number to the color illustrations in Grovers' book which we believe enhances the value of both books. A lesser number have been cross-referenced to Revi's, Whitlow's and Barret's.

In studying the prices in this book in conjunction with any of the illustrations in these other books it is well to keep in mind that many of them are very important pieces and well above the average in their classification. This difference may be due to a signature on the piece, documentation, color excellence, historical importance, or other special significance. While not all of them command premiums, many of them do and an allowance should be made in comparing those with others that appear to be the same or very similar. Any damage or imperfections in the piece compared will also be a very big factor in pricing.

A comparison with older price guides will show that many prices have changed. Most of the changes have been upward. This is especially true of the finer examples. The gap between these and their lesser "country cousins" continues to widen as more people are attracted to this field and others who have been interested for a number of years become more knowledgeable. The accuracy of this guide is better on the less important pieces than it is on the rare ones for the rather obvious reason that there are many more exchanges in the commoner pieces. Some of the most important pieces appear so infrequently that there is little or no basis for comparison. The transactions in these are more likely to be negotiated affairs, done privately between two parties, than at public sales or auctions.

For those who are using the guide for the first time and are relatively uniformed about art glass, we highly recommend seeking out one of the reputable, recognized authorities in this area when you are buying, selling or merely obtaining information. Your chance of error and disappointment is greatly lessened and often at a lower cost. While this guide is a help, it is no substitute for knowledge and experience acquired in the market place.

GENERAL INFORMATION

There are numerous ways of obtaining more knowledge on this absorbing hobby. One prime source of information is the several magazines that specialize in the field of antiques and collecting, such as *Antiques Journal, Hobbies, Spinning Wheel* and the *Antiques Magazine*. Others are very helpful in keeping current on prices because of the large volume of advertising they carry, such as the *Antique Trader* and *Collectors News*. Antique shows, flea markets and auctions that are held all over the United States offer an excellent opportunity to see and to actually examine many pieces at close range. These events also make it possible to discuss individual questions with a number of very knowledgeable collectors and dealers.

Syndicated columnists like Ralph and Terry Kovel offer valuable information and advice. Their column *Know Your Antiques* appears in many publications. Books, many of which are listed on other pages, are constantly being referred to by the expert as well as the novice. The authors of these have done much independent research to add to the general knowledge and enjoyment of collecting bottles. Museums are an exceptionally rich source of accurate information. The curators or their assistants are often available to supplement the normal displays. Some of them conduct annual forums that occassionally offer another means of keeping abreast of the latest developments and personal contact with many experts. Two well known ones are the Corning Glass Museum and the Henry Ford Museum.

One of the most fruitful experiences a collector can have is an invitation to view and discuss the private collection of a leading authority in this area of interest. Such persons have accumulated impressive displays of all grades of desirability and in the process have learned some extremely valuable lessons that can be of great assistance to one fortunate enough to merit a visit with him. Most such advanced collectors are quite generous in giving their time and obtain real satisfaction in sharing their collection and anecdotes associated with them.

One of the very intriguing and satisfying rewards of collecting fine American Art Glass is the opportunity to uncover new information about the articles themselves, the men who made them, and the methods and materials they used. Discovering where, who, when, and how individual pieces were actually made is a thrilling adventure. All of the absorbing elements of one of the best selling "Who Done It" books are present. The great difference is that you are the detective and the one responsible for adding very essential and needed information from which many others will obtain enjoyment. In such cases a real obligation is inherent. That is to publish such information in some magazine or book for the benefit of all the others who are eager to acquire additional knowledge.

There seems to be an ever increasing emphasis on signed pieces as evidenced by the excessive premium such pieces will command over an equally meritorious unsigned one. Such blind reliance and investment in signed pieces is not always justified or wise. Today some signatures are being forged. These will never bother the astute collector as he will buy on the merit of the piece, signed or unsigned. At present many bargains are available to him on unsigned pieces.

The above remarks do not apply to specially autographed or marked examples. These have special historical significance and value.

HOW TO USE PRICE INFORMATION

The prices shown on the following pages were compiled to assist collectors, appraisers, and dealers in arriving at a fair approximation of the value of any piece of glass similar to the one thousand that are listed here and to thousands of others by fully understanding the basis on which these prices were obtained and the factors entering into the determination of value. Please remember that the prices shown here are unlikely to be the price of the next sale of what appears to be an identical piece. These prices are only a guide as to value and represent as near as it is possible to do so the mid-point in a range of prices that are paid at different times, by different people, in different locations, and under different conditions for the same piece. When used as a guide they can be extremely helpful as the basis for forming a fair appraisal of a similar piece.

The figures shown for each piece were arrived at by consulting with at least ten experts, some by long distance phone. All of these people have superior knowledge due to years of experience in collecting or selling the articles listed here. To these consultations we added valuable information obtained at the large auctions where there were many informed buyers competing on equal terms with each other, and who had a chance to thoroughly inspect the items beforehand. A composite figure was selected, not an average, that seemed to most fairly represent what an experienced collector would be likely to pay to an authorative dealer for an item he wanted to add to his collection. The selected price may surprise some readers as being much higher than they expected, especially those that are cross-referenced to a book such as Grovers'. This surprise is justified, as the prices are above average because the pieces illustrated in most books are carefully selected and documented pieces. They have to be. As such they will always command a premium price over an identical one of uncertain origin, unsigned, or not documented. The amount of premium varies with many factors. Knowledge on the part of the buyer is one. If the style or the color is exceptional, added value is certain. Since some of the pieces listed and illustrated have been reproduced in later years, the value of such a piece might vary in the ratio of from ten to one depending on the possibility that it is a fake or genuine.

We have intentionally cross-referenced as many pieces as possible to color illustrations in this guide or other books since it affords the opportunity of comparing a specific object as it really appears and not depending so much on visualization. It will pay big dividends to study these prices and pictures together. At the same time note the size and whether or not the piece is signed. A signature or good documentation can add from twenty-five to one hundred percent to the price, sometimes more. The color is another factor to remember. Off color will cause a marked reduction in price while a superb example may bring high rewards.

CRITICAL CONDITION AND COLOR

The value of any antique or collectible is closely related to the condition of the object at the time of purchase. Art Glass is no exception. Since we are interested in price at the time of sale we are also interested in the condition of the object at that time and not when found or acquired.

The prices shown in this book are for articles in mint condition. This means *NO* scratches, chips, stains, discoloration, cracks or missing portions. Those that do not meet these qualifications, and there will be many, should sell for less than the price quoted by some percentage figure. This could be ten percent less for very minor scratches or nicks on desirable pieces to as much as ninety percent when the piece is in rough or damaged condition. This is especially so if there are a plentiful supply of perfect examples at reasonable prices. There are many collectors who will not compromise their goal of collecting only perfect samples, even for rare specimens. However, the great majority seem to bend more when the article in question is very scarce or rare. When well known museums will display repaired or imperfect examples of great rarities it seems a good policy to follow, as long as appropriate concessions are made on price.

As the price of most Art Glass continues to outpace inflation, there will be more and more need for collectors to pay close attention to the pieces they purchase. As time goes on, they will have passed through several hands and during this process may have been altered to upgrade their appearance with the sole purpose of deceiving the purchaser into paying more than justified by their intrinsic worth. The common term for this procedure is faking. Other repairs, restorations, reissues, or reproductions have their place and price if they are labeled as such. One thing in favor of glass is that many imperfections cannot successfully be disguised or hidden. One of these is cracks, which show up distinctly in clear glass and are noticeable in any colored piece. Many collectors are making more use of the "black light" (ultra-violet) lamps which will show up most of the deviations from a perfect, genuine article. Many dealers have them for the use and protection of their customers. Any of the normal cleaning methods which are necessary obviously should not be considered as unethical techniques as they are simply restorative operations which are to be expected and desired before sale or display.

In considering the value of any piece of Art Glass the color as well as the condition may be of utmost importance. Probably the prices of the various types of Peachblows are as sensitive to color variations as any one category. In general deep rich colors are the prime examples. The other shaded glasswares such as Burmese and Amberina, are other examples. Whenever possible it is advisable to refer to a color picture of the piece for which the price is given. In many cases in the book a comment on the adequacy of the color for that particular example and price is made.

Tiffany and Steuben pieces have many variations in their iridescent pieces as might be expected from any handmade articles. In addition to the variations within a color there is also the scarcity of certain colors that made them particularly valuable. Any piece of red iridescent Tiffany or Steuben is rare. The greens and blues command a premium as compared to the gold iridescence.

While the title of this section only mentions color and condition, the other attribute of overall quality is of equal if not greater importance in many pieces of Art Glass. This encompasses the intrinsic design and execution of the piece. This is one reason why all French Cameo does not sell for the same price.

CLASSIFICATIONS OF ART GLASS

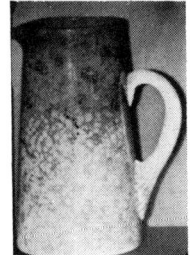

2600

AGATA GLASS

An opaque shaded glass with the same coloring as New England Peachblow (Wild Rose). A deep rose at the top fading to creamy white at the bottom. It is distinguished by splotches or spots on the surface that were produced by further treatments of the original heat-sensitive glass. This was developed and patented by Joseph Locke. The deeper the color and the more pronounced the splotches, the more desirable the piece. Very high priced in good color and condition. Unsigned but identified by unique coloring.

Grover Plate Numbers
90. Pitcher, water 8½", excellent coloring. R-p57   2600
91. Cruet, vinegar, mint condition and good color.   1250
92b Vase, celery, 8" fair coloring, square top.   750
93. Vase, morgan shape, mint base. R-p58   3000
94. Vase, lily shape, 8", good color.   1200
95. Vase, stick, 8", fine dark color and figures.   1500

Other Examples
1. Bowl, crimped top, 6"H. Light color   370
2. Bowl, finger. 3½"D. Ruffled edge. Exceptional color. 850
3. Mug, lemonade. 7"H. Low handle. Good coloring.   700
4. Punch Cup, superb mottling and color.   400
5. Set, condiment, 3 piece in silver holder.   900
6. Toothpick, tricorn. Weak color.   185
7. Toothpick, pinched top. Average color   300
8. Tumbler, excellent mottling and color.   450
9. Tumbler, water. Good coloring.   295
10. Tumbler, water. Fairly good coloring.   275
11. Tumbler, water. Fair color and mottle.   250
12. Tumbler, water. Faint mottling, light color.   160

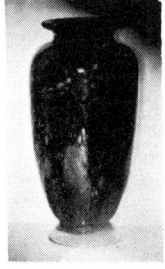

2500

AGATE GLASS

A varied-colored opaque glass made to resemble the agate stone in rich shades of browns, tans, and yellows. Best known examples are those produced by Tiffany and Steuben. The correct term for the Steuben product is Moss Agate. Examples of either type are vary scarce. Not always signed.

Grover Plate Numbers
202 Vase, 5", Tiffany, signed.   2000
203 Vase, 8½", Tiffany, signed.   2600
204 Vase, 6", Tiffany, signed.   2200
205 Vase, 10", Tiffany, signed.   2000

Other Examples
1. Shade, lamp, Steuben Moss Agate, Rk-p25   750
2. Vase, 10"H, Steuben Moss Agate, Rk-p25   2500
3. Vase, 15"H, blue, Steuben Moss Agate, Gd-XXXI   3500
4. Vase, 10"H, Steuben Moss Agate, Gd-XXXI   2600

ALBERTINE GLASS

An opaque decorated product of the Mt. Washington Glass Company which was later called Crown Milano. For more details refer to Crown Milano. Examples would be classed as such unless it had the earlier Albertine name on it. This ware was also called, "Dresden" in advertisements in the late 1800's.

1. Vase, 13", white to green & gold enamel.   165
2. Vases, pr. w/portrait medallions. $11\frac{1}{2}$". Signed.   550

ALEXANDRITE GLASS

A product of Thomas Webb factory in England that is a heat-sensitive glass which, after treatment, shades from blue to amber with some red or fushia tones. This may be confused with pieces produced by other sources and techniques. For more details on this type of shading, refer to the section on Bluerina.

750

Grover Plate Numbers
339 Glass, wine, $4\frac{1}{2}$", thumbprint pattern.   750
340 Plate, 6", rippled edge, fine coloring.   450
341a Pitcher, cream, 3", thumbprint   1000
341b Plate, $5\frac{1}{2}$", crimped edge, thumbprint   425

Other Examples
1. Bowl, finger & under plate, honeycomb. Excep. coloring.   1250
2. Bowl & tray, rare, ruffled edges, 6"D.   875
3. Bowl, finger, ruffled top. No plate. Weak color. 350
4. Vase, honeycomb ruffled top. 6"H. Light coloring. 350
5. Toothpick, $2\frac{1}{2}$"H, fine coloring.   650
6. Toothpick, $2\frac{1}{2}$"H, good color shading.   450

AMBERETTE GLASS

This is a frosted and stained (yellow) pressed glass formed in a mold and commonly known as Klondike. It is questionable that this product should be classified as Art Glass, but since it is appearing in important sales and auctions, a few pieces are listed below. Speculative. Prices have wide range. Pieces are unsigned and identified by characteristic pattern as most such pressed glass wares are.

80

1. Dish, butter, covered, square . . . 125
2. Dish, sauce, frosted and stained, 4" . . . 50
3. Goblet, water, 5½"H, footed. . . . 85
4. Pitcher, water, 8", frosted and stained . . . 125
5. Tumbler, water, 4", frosted and stained . . . 75
6. Set, creamer and sugar, covered bowl. . . . 175

AMBERINA GLASS

One of the best known of the Art Glasses. It was patented by the New England Glass Company. Technically known as a transparent parti-colored and shaded glass with the best examples having a deep fuschia color at the top and graduating to a deep amber color at the base. This dual color shading was produced by careful reheating of the top portion of the piece which then changed from amber to fuschia because of a gold compound which was added to the batch. Not scarce, but good examples and shapes are desirable additions to any collection. Originally produced in the 1880's, it was later made by Libbey Glass Company in the 1920's. Some later pieces of this production are found signed "Libbey."

350

Grover Plate Numbers
1. Jar, covered, 8-3/4", good color. Diamond Quilted . . . 200
2. Jar, covered, low 4½", signed Libbey. Excellent color. . . . 300
3. Pitcher, creamer, 6", engraved. Rare. . . . 500
4. Vase, celery, 6½", light color, Diamond Quilted. . . . 120
5. Pitcher, creamer, 4", fluted. . . . 200
6. Pitcher, water, 7½", rope handle . . . 350
7. Vase, pedestal and fluted top, 7", deep color. . . . 275
8. Bowl, finger, 5" diam. ribbed. . . . 100
9. Sauce, square D & B pressed design. . . . 75
10. Vase, 5", stork pattern. . . . 275

Other Examples
1. Bowl, 10"D, bronze stand. Hand painted enamel decor. . . . 375
2. Bowl, finger. Diamond Quilted. Light color. . . . 40
3. Cruet, inverted thumbprint. Original stopper. . . . 105
4. Epergne, Baccarat, bronze mounts on onyx footed plinth. . . . 150
5. Pitcher, water. Reverse coloring, 9½". . . . 150
6. Pitcher, water. Inverted thumbprint, ribbed handle, 9". . . . 200
7. Pitcher, water. 8". Fine deep coloring, engraved pattern. . . . 450
8. Plate, square. Marked HIG on bee, 7½" wide. . . . 40
9. Punch Cup, Diamond Quilted, excellent color. . . . 80
10. Punch Cup. Inverted thumbprint. Light color. . . . 35
11. Punch Cup. Reversed Diamond Quilted enamel decor. . . . 55
12. Punch Cup. Inverted thumbprint. . . . 80
13. Punch Cup. . . . 70
14. Salt & Pepper Shakers, decorated. . . . 75
15. Toothpick, 2"H, N.E. ovoid, deep color, D.Q. . . . 115
16. Toothpick, tricorn, Diamond Quilted. . . . 75
17. Toothpick, reversed tricorn, Diamond Quilted. . . . 95
18. Toothpick, reversed, inverted thumbprint. . . . 130

19. Toothpick, D.Q., square mouth. N.Eng.	100
20. Toothpick, ruffled top, inverted baby thumbprint.	125
21. Toothpick, pr. gl., footed. Daisy & button. Revi p29	180
22. Toothpick, Diamond Quilted, tricorn.	105
23. Tumbler, swirled.	60
24. Tumbler, Diamond Quilted.	85
25. Tumbler, reversed hobnail.	110
26. Tumbler, reversed inverted hobnail.	40
27. Tumbler, Diamond Quilted.	50
28. Tumbler, ribbed.	80
29. Tumbler, drape.	70
30. Tumblers, set of 6.	390
31. Vase, bud, trumpet shaped. $7\frac{1}{2}$".	150
32. Vase, 6"H, good color.	90

380

AVENTURINE GLASS

Produced for hundreds of years by incorporating very fine particles which appear under the surface of the glass like fine gold or silver dust. Much of the present day Venetian glass secures this effect by rolling the gather of hot glass on a table sprinkled with bronze (gold) powder. The collectible types were produced during the Victorian era. They are sometimes confused with Spangle or Vasa Murrhina. Made by different companies in America and Europe and mostly unsigned.

Grover Plate Numbers
402 Pitcher, water, 7", opaque red w/D.Q. design.   225

Other Examples
1. Jug, water, large handle, scatter pattern. R-p104   275
2. Tumbler, swirl ribbed, blue w/gold.   75
3. Vase, urn shaped, handles, black and gold. R-p106   385

160

BACCARAT GLASS

Products of this well-known French glass manufacturer have been produced for over one hundred years in a great abundance of many types and kinds. Even now, they will produce any of their old patterns on special order. Famous for their old paperweights made prior to and shortly after 1850, and re-introduced again in 1950 with limited editions of millefiore and commemorative sulphides of prominent persons. They also produce a distinctive type of amberina which shades from a reddish orange to clear. Usually found in swirled and ribbed bottles and jars.

Grover Plate Numbers
375 Vase, French Cameo, signed, 8"H   200

Amberina Examples
1. Epergne, marble base, 15", swirled amberina W-p20-1   160
2. Bottle, cologne, 5", amberina swirled. W-p20-2   50
3. Candlesticks, pair, swirled & footed. W-p20-4   100
4. Bowl & Mugs, amberina, thumbprint pattern. 11 mugs.   900
5. Candlesticks, pair amberina, swirl, 7". Impf.   50
6. Compote, candy, amberina. Signed. 4".   100
7. Lamp columns, pr. amberina twisted, periodic, 18".   125

Paperweight Examples
1. Paperweight, fulphide, faceted, clear, Martin Luther   150
2. Paperweight, sulphide, faceted, clear, J. F. Kennedy   250
3. Paperweight, sulphide, faceted, red&white overlay Kennedy   850
4. Paperweight, tight packed canes, dated 1956   150
5. Paperweight, scattered canes on muslin ground, dated 1846   700

Cameo Examples
1. Goblet, engraved vine & grape in gold, 5", signed.   80
2. Vase, acid finished, coiled snake decor., 8", signed.   175

BLUERINA GLASS

A controversial classification used by a number of Art Glass enthusiasts to refer to a transparent shaded glass that gradually changes from blue to amber. A name coined from Amberina which has the fuschia to amber shading. Since there were a number of methods of producing shaded glasses and used by several different glass houses here and in Europe, the boundaries of this term Bluerina are not well defined. For example, some people may include Alexandrite glass which has similar shading and is the specific name for a product of Thomas Webb Company of England according to Mr. Revi. The Grovers own a pitcher, which they call Painted Amberina, attributed to Boston & Sandwich Glass Company. This is illustrated in their book on page 180. Others might call it Bluerina. As a result of this vagueness of classification, a wide difference of opinion exists as to its rarity and value. A well-documented bowl of Alexandrite would be worth several hundred dollars while another of uncertain origin and merit might bring less than fifty dollars. Buy this type only from reliable sources.

1. Vases, blue to purple, thorn decor., 10". W-p22.   175

BOHEMIAN GLASS

60

A broad classification of various types of glass made in the Western part of Czechoslovakia that was formerly called Bohemia. In common usage it refers to a well-known crystal glass fashed or cased with a rich red and then engraved through the red so that the matte design stands out against the red background. Most often the design consists of woodland scenes. This is correctly known as Egermann technique, after the man who developed the style. This copper wheel engraving is frequently found in deer and pine tree designs. Bohemian glass has been made continuously since it was introduced and is still in production in both

Czechoslovakia and in Venice. For this reason, examples are not scarce and the age is usually in question. As a result, the prices have not kept pace with many of comparable merit and age. This style was also made in other colors, such as yellow, blue and tri-colored, the latter being quite unusual. Many other types and styles of glass were produced in Bohemia; these are classified under their specific names such as Loetz, Lithyalin, Moser, and Enameled Glass. Contrary to the opinion of many people, pieces of great artistic merit and value have been produced in this area as shown by examples in all the great museums.

1. Bowl, w/cover, tray, ladle, 10 glasses. Enamel & gold.   250
2. Bowl, cranberry overlay, hand painted decoration.   60
3. Candlesticks, very fine cut glass, yel-br base & top.   30
4. Chalice, footed & fluted, 6", ruby to clear, deer.   60
5. Decanter, slim, 12", cut panels & etched designs. Red.   80
6. Decanter & Glasses, ruby red. 6 glasses.   75
7. Decanters, set of 3 Egermann, orig. stoppers. Amber   160
8. Goblet, ruby etched to clear in vintage pattern   35
9. Holders, candlestick, pr. ruby Egermann, hand etched, $8\frac{1}{2}$"   50
10. Pokal, covered. 8", ruby to clear in scenic design, c. 1925   50
11. Tumblers, water, set 6, red engraved to clear, c. 1940   95
12. Urn, covered, 22" H. Deer & woodland decor.   175
13. Vase, tri-colored, bl. yel. & red, cut windows, 10".   125
14. Vases, pr. ruby Egermann, engraved, 10".   100
15. Vase, Flower, amber. Engraved.   85
16. Wine, footed, knob stem, very dark red, monkey design.   20

BOSTON & SANDWICH GLASS

For examples and description refer to the section on Sandwich Glass. The names of the products of the Boston & Sandwich Glass Company of Cape Cod are commonly shortened to this form.

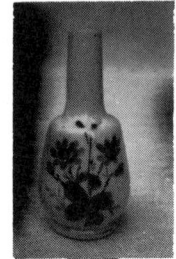
50

BRISTOL GLASS

This term usually refers to a semi-opaque white glass hand decorated in colored enamels which originated in the Bristol district of England where it was made by a number of glasshouses as well as in America during the Victorian period. Not generally classified as an Art Glass, possibly because of its abundance and the fact that is was originally inexpensive cottage type glassware. Now medium priced in the twenty to forty dollar price range, some of the better pieces are beginning to escalate in price and others may be expected to follow.

1. Basket, pink opaline, bird, ruffled edge, $10\frac{1}{2}$".   100
2. Bottle, Eng., w/"Rum" in gold & flat stopper, cobalt blue.   120
3. Bowl, 7" lily shape, amethyst, blown.   20
4. Ewer, English. Decor. satin glass w/metal base & mount.   100
5. Jar, rose w/cover. Blue pink enameled.   60
6. Lamp, oil, Eng., with hand painted floral decor.   325
7. Lamp, hurricane, green opaline w/6 arms.   350

8. Tumbler, yellow w/tulip decor. 15
9. Urn, w/cover, hand painted floral decor., 15". 40
10. Vase, 10" green enameled glass w/handles. 70
11. Vase, 10" pink & gold enameled flowers. 65
12. Vase, 13½" purple tinted enameled. 55
13. Vase, opaline, hand painted decor. 11-3/4". 70
14. Vases, pr. off white opaline table. Decorated. 6½". 50

1000

BURMESE GLASS

A shaded opaque glass originally produced by the Mt. Washington Glass Co., it was covered by a patent issued to Frederick Shirley and assigned to the company. This is another one of the heat sensitive glasses that obtain a blush pink color at the top from the action of the gold in the compound in the reheating process. This pink color shades gradually to the original pale yellow obtained from having added Uranium in the original mix. It was produced in natural shiny finish and in soft matte finish by acid treatment. Later, Thos. Webb & Sons of England was licensed to make this under the name of Queen's Burmese. A later reproduction made some thirty years ago by the Gunderson Glass Company has lighter colors and less delicate execution but is acquiring a substantial following as Gunderson Burmese, which see.

Grover Plate Numbers
37a Cruet, vinegar, shiny finish, 7", light coloring 450
37b Cruet, vinegar, acid finish, 7", good coloring. 500
38. Vase, 13½" tall, ruffled foot and top, exc. color. 575
39. Vase, 12", handles, fine coloring. 475
40. Vase, 10", enamel decoration, handles. 2400
41. Lamp w/chimney, 14"decorated, unusual. 2000
42a Vase, 10", enamel in Queen's Design, exc. color. 1000
42b Tumbler, 4", Queen's Design, fine coloring 450
42c Vase, footed trumpet. Queen's Design, fine color. 850
43. Vase, 12½", painted desert scene and gold. 4000
44. Pitcher, cream, 5½", hobnail and decorated. 1250
45. Lamp, Fairy, 11", signed T. Webb & Clarke 1000
46. Pitcher, water, 9", enamel decoration and verse. 1000
47. Ewer, 9", squat dome w/enamel decoration. 950
48a Pitcher, creamer, 3½", wishbone feet. 400
48b Bowl, sugar, 3½", wishbone feet. 375
49. Bowl, 4", rigaree around neck. 475
50. Bowl, 4", fluted edge, excellent coloring. 360
51. Bowl, 6½", applied Burmese decoration, footed. 850
52. Jug, syrup, 6", enamel decoration, silver top. 700

Other Examples
1. Bell, with handle, 6½". Weak color. 110
2. Bell, rare, emerald green handle, 11-3/4" H. 550
3. Bottle, perfume, w/cut stopper. Light color. 95
4. Bottle, cologne. Enamel floral decor. Sterl. top. Hallmark 275
5. Bowl, berry, with scalloped rim, 12". 475

Other Examples Burmese cont'd

6. Bowl, $2\frac{1}{2}$", shiny, w/ruffled top — 210
7. Bowl, finger, shiny, ruffled top. — 185
8. Bowl, 12"D, rare overlay decor., Mt. Wash. Glass Co. — 175
9. Bowl, miniature rose, floral decor. — 160
10. Bowl, 4" x 5", yellow to pink. — 190
11. Bowl, rose, crimped top. Miniature. — 120
12. Dish, candy, 5"D, Mt. Wash., w/ruffled edge. — 400
13. Dish, nut, small with ruffled edge. — 270
14. Dish, nut, ruffled edge, light color. — 160
15. Dish, nut. — 175
16. Goblet, $6\frac{1}{2}$", very fine, cream to rose color. — 275
17. Hat, 4"H, shiny, good color. — 250
18. Lamp, fairy, with Clark base. Dome shape. — 175
19. Lamp base, fairy, w/folded square top. Signed. — 165
20. Lamp, fairy, Clark base, impf. — 100
21. Lamps, fairy (3), Webb, w/3 bud vases on brass frame. — 1300
22. Pitcher, cream in Webb Burmese, as is. — 80
23. Toothpick holder, decor., Mt. Wash., 3 sided folded top. — 285
24. Toothpick holder, Queen Burmese, Webb, paper label, 3". — 280
25. Toothpick, ruffled top, rigaree decor. Excellent color. — 300
26. Toothpick, tricorn enamel, daisey decoration. — 365
27. Toothpick, tricorn, enamel decoration. — 250
28. Set, Condiment, Mt. Wash. with silver plated stand. — 800
29. Toothpick, tricorn, D.Q., enamel daisy decor. Weak color. — 200
30. Toothpick, tricorn, blackberry decor. — 160
31. Toothpick, shiny, Diamond Quilted. — 175
32. Toothpick, square mouth, Diamond Quilted. — 150
33. Tumbler, decor. Queen's, signed Thomas Webb. — 375
34. Tray, $3\frac{1}{2}$"D, Mt. Wash., average color. — 150
35. Tumbler, water, $3\frac{1}{2}$"H, shiny, good color. — 170
36. Tumbler, water, yellow to pink. — 150
37. Tumbler, water, maidenhair fern decoration. — 225
38. Tumbler, water, floral decoration. — 200
39. Tumbler, water, 3-1/4"H. — 155
40. Tumbler, water, average color. — 135
41. Vase, 3", w/square top, medium color. — 150
42. Vase, egg, footed, decor., good color. — 275
43. Vase, footed, tricorn top, 10", fine coloring, floral decor. — 550
44. Vase, hex. top, shiny, decor., fine color. — 250
45. Vase, Jack-in-Pulpit, hand painted enamel decor. 6-3/4". — 550
46. Vase, lily shape in silver holder, $12\frac{1}{2}$". — 400
47. Vase, Queen's, 4"H, signed Thomas Webb, decorated. — 375
48. Vase, $2\frac{1}{2}$" miniature, hexagon top, light coloring. — 125
49. Vase, miniature $2\frac{1}{2}$"H, crimped top, decor., light. — 250
50. Vase, Mt. Wash., decor. flowers & leaves. — 550
51. Vase, $4\frac{1}{2}$" petal top w/blue bird decor, sgn'd Thomas Webb. — 400
52. Vase, on stand, petite, morning glory shape. — 225
53. Vase, pinched top, shiny, sgn'd Thomas Webb. — 375
54. Vase, Queen's, Webb, square top, hand painted decor. — 300

Burmese Glass

55.	Vase, double handle, 15"H, rare, enamel. yel. to pink.	3800
56.	Vase, ribbed, footed, pinched top, 6"H, berry pontil.	250
57.	Vase, ribbed, ruffled top, 5"H, satin finish.	180
58.	Vase, ruffled top on ruffled feet, good color. Floral decor.	270
59.	Vase, satin finish, 8-1/4", good coloring.	275
60.	Vase, shiny, ruffled top, 4"H.	195
61.	Vase, slender, 26", yellow to pale pink.	375
62.	Vase, small acid, petal top, sgn'd Thomas Webb.	300
63.	Vase, small ruffled top. Light colors.	170
64.	Vase, small ruffled top. Weak coloring.	125
65.	Vase, square top, $2\frac{1}{2}$", delicate enamel floral decor.	240
66.	Vase, small square top, floral decor., weak color.	155
67.	Vase, small, D.Q., square top, light colors.	155
68.	Vase, small hexagon top, dull finish, average color.	200
69.	Stand, w/2 yel/pink shades, 2 sm. & 1 lg. vase.	700
70.	Vase, Queen's, Webb, petite, 5 sided folded edge.	475

18

CAMBRIDGE GLASS

Refers to glass made by the Cambridge Glass Co. of Ohio, not the products of the New England Glass Company of Cambridge Mass. This Ohio firm made a number of different kinds of glass, principally pressed. One popular type is Tuscan ware. Some items are marked with a "C" in a triangle. Not strictly an "Art Glass" the products are being actively collected and sold along with other identifiable glass. One characteristic piece is the shallow bowl champagne in crystal or color with a satin glass nude figure for the stem.

1.	Basket, amethyst glass.	20
2.	Bowl, Tuscan. Light irid. on separated black vase, $9\frac{1}{2}$"D.	35
3.	Bowl, amethyst glass, $9\frac{1}{2}$".	30
4.	Candlesticks, pr., dolphin shape, flamingo color, $10\frac{1}{2}$".	40
5.	Swan, black glass, signed.	25
6.	Wine, champagne, crystal w/satin nude figure stem.	18

950

CAMEO GLASS—AMERICAN

Glass with an incised surface is referred to by a number of names such as Cameo, Intaglio, Carved, Engraved, Etched and Acid Cut Back to name the principal ones. True Cameo Glass was hand carved like the cameo stone jewelry. See Cameo-English for a detailed description. The short cut process of using acid to eat away some of the surface to create a design superseded the hand carving and wheel engraving. Even so, these later pieces of English and French origin are still referred to as "Cameo." The same process for Steuben wares is called Acid Cut Back, for Tiffany pieces either Intaglio or Cameo is used. For Honesdale the word is Etched

2700

CAMEO GLASS — CHINESE

The Chinese have produced fine cameo glass pieces on two-color cased glass as well as jade for hundreds of years. Sometimes this has been referred to as Peking Glass. As with other types of cameo, the examples from the end of the Nineteenth Century or later are the ones that are usually referred to today. One relatively common form is the snuff bottle in which the age and quality vary tremendously. Some of these are jade and some are glass. They may range in price from twenty dollars to several hundred dollars and more.

2500

CAMEO GLASS — ENGLISH

Refers to a double-layered glass produced in the last part of the Nineteenth Century. The first, or inner, layer was usually a dark color and the casing, or outer, layer was white. Originally the piece was hand carved leaving the design white relief with many graduations obtained by varying the depth of carving. Later this carving was done with engraving wheels and finally by using acid to produce what is known as acid cut back (ACB). Most very early pieces are in museums, but good examples of floral vases done with engraving wheels are still obtainable. This technique was first revived by John Northwood about 1850.

Grover Plate Numbers

308 Vase, 12", gourd shape, horseman, S & W.	2000
309 Vase, 8", rose floral, Stevens & Williams, signed.	1000
310 Vase, 5", white on blue floral, signed S & W.	750
311 Vase, 4", Dolce-Relievo, S & W.	1050
312 Vase, 9", white on red, signed S & W.	875
313 Vase, 7", white on tan, signed S & W.	700
314 Vase, $9\frac{1}{2}$", three color, signed Webb.	500
315 Vase, 8", M.O.P. white on red, Webb Illus.	2500
316 Vase, 9", three color, signed Webb.	1600
317 Vase, $12\frac{1}{2}$", simulated ivory, signed Webb.	1500
318 Vase, 9", three color, signed Webb.	1400
319 Vase, $5\frac{1}{2}$", three color, signed Webb.	2000
320 Vase, 10", white on red, signed Webb.	1800
321 Vase, 7", three layer cameo, signed Webb.	2000
322 Vases, 5", pair, ivory cameo, signed Webb.	1600
323 Vase, 6", cameo and applied color, signed Webb.	950
324 Plate & finger bowl, 6", both signed Webb.	1100
325 Vase, $11\frac{1}{2}$", white on red, signed Webb.	1000
326 Vase, 18", five color, Webb type.	2250
327 Inkwell, 6", three color, Webb type.	575
328 Bottle, $9\frac{1}{2}$", three color whiskey.	600
329 Bowl, 6", white dragons on blue, Webb type.	1100
330 Bowl, $4\frac{1}{2}$", folded rim, Webb type.	1000
331 Vase, $4\frac{1}{2}$", Chien Lyng, Revi 152	1000
332 Vase, 9", Webb cameo ivory.	1250

Cameo Glass - English
333 Vase, 11½", simulated ivory. Webb type. 1400
334 Vase, 16", elaborate, white on red 2100
335 Vase, 7", blue with white figure, sgn'd Woodhall. 5800
336 Vase, 7½", tan with white figure, sgn'd Woodhall & Webb 6000
337 Plaque, 8", white figure on tan, sgn'd Woodhall. 3800
338 Vase, 13", white figures on tan, sgn'd Woodhall & Webb 6500

275

CAMEO GLASS — FRENCH

From the latter part of the 19th Century through the early years of the Twentieth Century, Emile Gallé dominated the field of French cameo glass and was also very instrumental in inspiring the production of a similar glass in the United States. Very fine pieces were made in the early years, but during the later period designs were simplified and produced entirely by cutting in the design with acid. A great deal of the French Cameo glass is distinguished by the predominance of earthy or autumnal colors of browns, golds, and reds. All of the other colors were used but much less frequently. Besides Gallé there were many other producers of this type, such as Daum in the city of Nancy. There are also those masters who are still producing glass there today. LeGras, DeVez, and Mueller Brothers, are some of the many less important designers and producers. Fortunately, a great deal of this type of glass is signed. The Gallé glass that has a star in front of the name was produced after Gallé died, according to most writers.

Grover Plate Numbers
355 Tumblers, 4", water, clear enameled, signed Galle. pr. 350
356 Goblet, 8", blue, floral, Galle 500
357 Vase, 11", brown and red floral. 375
358 Vase, 15", fruit and vine design, Galle. 350
359 Vase, 14", elaborate multi-colored floral. 475
360 Vase, 14", green with enameled florals. 300
361 Ashtray, 6", Pate de Verre cameo, A. Walter 400
362 Basket, 7", black, yellow and red floral, Daum 275
363 Vase, 11", shaded red and hellow mums, DeVez 300
364 Vase, 11½", red and lavender floral, Monthoye. 240
365 Vase, 9", Pate de Verre cameo, Argy-Rousseau. 750
366 Vase, 7", blue cameo floral and enamel, St. Louis 400
367 Vase, 8", matte crystal and fish, Muller Freres. 500
368 Vase, 12", long necked, brown and tan, E. Rego. 160
369 Vase, 8", red to black, blue foot, Richard. 125
370 Vase, 16", tri-color with enamel, Val St. Lambert. 400
371 Pitcher, 6", shaded orange and white, Schneider. 125
372 Vase, 5", dark marbled swirls, Sevres. 175
373 Vase, 12", browns and reds, ship, D'Argental. 350
374 Vase, 10", black to orange, DeL'Arte. 200
375 Vase, 8", matte crystal and enamel, Baccarat. 250
376 Vase, 6½", blue and lavender scenic, LeGras. 275
377 Ewer, 9", thistle design, Roux Chalon. 240
378 Vase, 8", brown and green, scenic, DeLatte 190

Other Examples   Cameo Glass - French

1. Atomizer, signed "Richard".   125
2. Bowl, covered, Daum, decorated w/leaves & berries.   225
3. Bowl, Degue, metal stand.   160
4. Bowl, covered, w/blue pedestal base, signed Denoy.   250
5. Bowl, finger and underplate.   180
6. Bowl, pedestal stand, 10½", signed.   175
7. Ewer, orchid pattern, 13", signed.   550
8. Glass, wine, with cut stem, canary and ruby.   135
9. Lamp, table, 19", gr. &pink flower design. Unsgn'd.   475
10. Lamp, night, mushroom type, red, pink, purple sgn'd Darboy 175
11. Lamp, "Muller Freres Lunerville".   900
12. Lamp, min. kerosene, rare, wh. flower over yel. unsgn'd. 350
13. Plate, blue & red thistle pattern, signed G. A. Rousseau. 350
14. Shade, 4½", signed Larrain.   35
15. Tumbler, liquer, floral, 2"H.   115
16. Vase, 4", purple on light spatter blue, signed Charder.   145
17. Vase, 6", carved intaglio w/blue corn. on clam broth. Damon 200
18. Vase, rare, Daum, burnt orange & lt. gr., signed.   700
19. Vase, bud, Daum, gold & emerald gr., bronze snake, sgn'd. 200
20. Vase, DeLatte, pale blue ground & amethyst decor., sgn'd. 300
21. Vase, 8", DeLatte, w/seascape & woodland scene.   200
22. Vase, flower, mt. castle & tree decor., sgn'd D'Anrys.   275
23. Vase, cobalt blue, signed Harroch, 8".   185
24. Vase, 5", w/tricorn top, floral decor., sgn'd Houdaille.   85
25. Vase, 9½", signed Koch.   150
26. Vase, LaMartine, pine tree design, 7½".   200
27. Vase, 4" oval, sgn'd Lamartine, summer scene at lake.   300
28. Vase, 4", signed LeGras, summer woodland scene on pink. 155
29. Vase, 6½", w/red Va. Creeper vine & berries. sgn'd LeGras. 210
30. Vase, rare enamel floral decor. w/bird, 12½", signed.   135
31. Vase, LeGras, signed.   200
32. Vase, LeGras, 17", signed.   150
33. Vase, bud, 10", LeGras, signed.   150
34. Vase, table, square, LeGras, 7-3/4", scenic decor.   170
35. Vase, footed, flower, signed LeVerre Francais.   200
36. Vase, table, 9½", signed LeVerre Francais.   125
37. Vase, petite, 6-3/4", LeVerre Francais.   110
38. Vase, bud, 6", signed Mazzi.   90

250

125

200

20

CARDER GLASS

See Steuben Glass for full details, pictures and prices. Strictly speaking any glass made by the Steuben Glass Company from 1903 to 1918 and by the Steuben Division of the Corning Glass Company from 1918 to 1932 is Carder glass. Frederick Carder the founder was solely responsible for all of the designs during these periods and for the formulations and development of the special colors and unique finishes developed during these years. A more descriptive term for this glass would be Carder Steuben Glass to distinguish it from the glass produced by the Steuben Division from 1932 to the present.

9000

CARMEL SLAG GLASS

The Indiana Tumbler & Goblet Company produced a number of interesting pressed glass articles at the turn of the century that today are highly collectible and being seen much more frequently in Art Glass sales and auctions. One of the products was known as Carmel Slag because of its color and the lighter color striations which permeated the base color at random. Other products of this company were Chocolate Glass and Holly Amber along with lesser known ones.

75

1. Bowls, glass, pair, 4"D. 38
2. Bowl, sugar, Dewey pattern. 20
3. Butter Dish, creamer & spooner, shell pattern. 75
4. Candlesticks, tall, in pressed design. 48
5. Creamer & Cruet, no stopper. Both 40
6. Dish, dolphin shape with fish cover. 55
7. Jug, syrup, with metal top, cactus pattern. 60
8. Spooner & Jar, not matching. Both 40

CORALENE GLASS

This refers to an applied decoration in the form of small glass beads which are usually colored and flourescent. The added decoration takes the form of branches of coral most frequently but other designs were used such as fleur-de-lis and diagonal double rows. The design was first painted on the ware with an adhesive to which the beads stuck. The piece was then fired, permanently fixing the beads. Most commonly applied to satin glass, it is sometimes found applied to Mother of Pearl Satin glass. It is more valuable applied to this type.

500

Lee Plate Number
21. Vase, 9", urn shape, vertical rainbow colors. 500

Grover Plate Numbers
117 Vase 6", MOP with flower and spray beading 375
118 Vase, 7", Burmese with yellow & red coral decor. 425
119 Vase, 7", green satin finish, red coral and flower. 340
120 Basket, 7", footed tan satin w/coral decoration. 500
121 Vase 8", butterscotch MOP with coral vari., illus. 575

Coralene Glass - cont'd

Other Examples
1. Basket, on peach blown type. Seaweed decor. 275
2. Decanter, w/stopper, 10", yellow seaweed decor. 50
3. Pitcher, 8", shaded blue satin, coral decoration. 350
4. Spooner, minor repair. 175
5. Tumbler, water, blue satin w/yellow decoration. 175
6. Vase, apricot, with two handles, ruffled top. 500
7. Vase, blue satin, crimped top w/yellow seaweed. Reg. No. 315
8. Vase, blue satin, with coral decoration, $5\frac{1}{2}$". 325
9. Vase, MOP, diamond quilted, pink, $6\frac{1}{2}$"W, zig-zag decor. 350
10. Vase, orange on white, 9", rare coloring. 600
11. Vase, pink satin miniature w/yellow wheat decoration. 175
12. Vase, pink satin overlay, 4"W, seaweed decoration. 70
13. Vases, pink satin, 9"W, gold seaweed decor., one w/reg. No 460
14. Vase, apricot to pearl, gold decor., $9\frac{1}{2}$". 350
15. Vase, yellow satin ovoid, 6", seaweed decor. 200

35

COSMOS GLASS

Highly identifiable type of stain decorated milk glass now appearing in some Art Glass sales and auctions. Usually pressed in a small all over diamond pattern with a band of stylized flowers at the top which are stained in blue, pink and yellow with a similar stained band in pink at the top. Not scarce but collectible.

1. Butter Dish, covered, w/polychrome flowers. 120
2. Lamp, miniature oil in clear glass w/brass base. 100
3. Lamp, kerosene, base only, cloth shade, $7\frac{1}{2}$". 40
4. Pitcher, milk glass water, good decoration. 90
5. Pitcher, water, 9"H. 105
6. Set, 5pcs. creamer, spoon, holder, S & P. 340
7. Tumblers, 8 matching, $3\frac{1}{2}$"H. Set 280
8. Tumblers, set of four, cornflower decor. Set 150

CRANBERRY GLASS

A pleasing light red transparent crystal made in many shades by untold numbers of makers for hundreds of years, even at the present time. As a result, this glass in general might not qualify under the term art glass in all cases. Many examples are described under specific makers, such as Carder's Steuben and Rubina, a shaded cranberry. Because of the large number of makers, wide range of quality, and uncertain age, the price of this glass varies widely. A few examples are given below of cranberry glass made during the Victorian period. Some of these can be safely attributed to this period because of silver mountings, shape, or applied decoration.

1. Bell, clear glass w/handle, 8"H. 45
2. Bell, white edging with clear handle. 85
3. Bell, swirl with clear handle, $7\frac{1}{2}$"H. 130
4. Compote, threaded with ruffled edge & base. 90
5. Creamer, applied clear glass handle. 40
6. Creamer, Eng., with applied glass handle. 35

Cranberry Glass Continued

7. Decanter, no stopper, 6". 30
8. Decanter, thumb print, clear prismatic stopper. 65
9. Decanter, applied handle, crystal, impf. 25
10. Dish, pie, crimp opalescent edge. 85
11. Epergne, English with three horns. 135
12. Lamp, study, w/matching shade & chimney. Unusual. 250
13. Lamp, Eng. oil, h.p.decor., thumb print globe, 18". 300
14. Lamp, miniature with shade. Hand enamel decorations. 110
15. Lamp, hanging, brass frame & chain. 250
16. Pitcher, water, rate, gold overlay, Bohemian. 135
17. Pitcher, water, clear glass handle. 65
18. Pitcher, small with clear glass handle. 50
19. Pitcher, water, thumbprint, ribbed clear glass handle. 20
20. Shaker, salt, satin glass, raindrop pattern. 50
21. Tumbler, shaded opalescent pattern. 35
22. Vase, ruffled top, 8". 40
23. Vase, slender, 10", enameled. 90
24. Vases, pr. 3-3/4", enameled. 28
25. Vase, flared edge with clear pedestal base, 6-3/4". 50
26. Vases, gold trim & hand painted enamel decoration. Pr. 100
27. Vases, Old Eng., appl. clear glass decoration. 8-1/4". Pr. 90
28. Vase, flower, ruffled edge, clear glass bottom. 45
29. Vases, trumpet shape, ruffled tops, 8½". Pr. 90

725

CROWN MILANO GLASS

A trade name and trademark which was registered by Mt. Washington Glass Company to identfy their highly developed technique for hand applied enamel decoration on opal glass in the later part of the Nineteenth Century. At first called Albertine and so labeled, it became known as Crown Milano as indicated by the CM in monogram form on the bottom. American and English manufacturers, in particular, made similar wares, but this product of Mt. Washington is typical of the elaborate decoration and colors in this type of glass. They are known for the same decorative style used on other types of their product. High quality and highly desirable collectors' items which are scarce today.

Grover Plate Numbers

53. Vase, Mt. Wash., bulbous, Chrysan.decor., 11", signed. 550
54. Vase, Mt. Wash. Dragon design in gold 15"H, signed. 675
55. Vase, 8½", swirled, wild fowl decoration, signed. 1500
56. Ewer, 10", twisted rope handle, panel decor., signed. 725
57. Pitcher, 12", white floral decoration, signed. 500
58. Vase, spherical, varied color floral, 5", signed. 450
59. Vase, 5½", covered scrolls and florals, signed. 750
60. Vase, 10½", jeweled, serpent overlay, signed. 575
61. Jar, biscuit, 9", leaves and light floral, signed. 425

Other Examples   Crown Milano Glass
1. Bowl, floral decor., heavy gold enamel, pairpoint holder.   450
2. Jar, buscuit, silver top and handle, exc. color, signed.   500
3. Pitcher, bulbous, gold decor., rural scene, 13½".   850
4. Vase, miniature, enamel leaf decor., 3", signed.   285
5. Vase, 14", bulbous, thin neck, heavily decor., signed.   420
6. Vase, bottle shaped, good decoration, signed.   320

150

CUSTARD GLASS

Another pressed glass variation of opaque milk glass obtained by adding color to produce a heavy cream color. Those pieces marked with an "N" for the first producer, The Northwood Glass Company, command a premium over unmarked pieces that were made by others. This glass was popular around 1900 and the molds that produced this in some twenty patterns were also used to produce the very inexpensive (at that time) Carnival Glass. Because of the interesting patterns and wide range of shapes this relatively scarce glass is now being seen more frequently in Art Glass sales because of the prices it now commands as indicated below. See Pink Slag section for a still higher priced cousin which comes in the same Inverted Fan pattern.

1. Bowl, oval, argonaut shell, 11"D.   200
2. Bowls, set of 5 berry, gold trim decor.   Set   125
3. Bowl, oval, baked gold decorations, 5".   75
4. Bowl, gold decoration, 8½".   45
5. Dish, butter, w/inverted fern pattern   200
6. Cruet, vinegar, grape pattern, original stopper   150
7. Compote, footed Louis IV decor.   70
8. Pitcher, water w/3 tumblers. Blue Chrysan. imperfect.   175
9. Set, water pitcher & 6 tumblers, argonaut shell.   450
10. Toothpick, blue, signed Northwood, Chrysan. sprig.   275
11. Tumbler, blue, Chrysan. sprig.   90

800

CUT GLASS

Cut glass of the so-called Brilliant Period, extending from the last quarter of the Nineteenth Century to World War I, has not always been classed as Art Glass even though most of this type was contemporary with the many types of colored glass. Even some of it was colored and made in the same factories, such as Steuben and Libbey. Many times the best of these pieces required more time and skill to produce than their cousins with higher sounding names. Today thing are changing rapidly with the discovery of some of the fine intaglio pieces of Hawkes Gravic Glass and Tuthill, and the entirely different design types of Steuben such as the beautiful, rare birds like the Peacock and Pheasant. Evidence of this is the prices being paid for fine artistic examples of pure lead crystal with superb workmanship. The price of twenty-three hundred dollars for an elaborately cut coffee pot at a very recent auction is strong evidence that this neglected Art Glass has "arrived." Signed pieces usually command a premium of up to 50%.

Cut Glass - cont'd

1. Basket, 6", round w/loop handle, all over cut — 90
2. Basket, 8", pinched and flared top, elaborate cut, engraved — 200
3. Basket, 18", flared top and all over cutting, sgn'd Hoare — 425
4. Bowl, punch, 14" on pedestal, heavy cutting. — 600
5. Bowl, rose, 8", fine hobstars and splits. — 90
6. Bowl, berry, 8", signed Hawkes. — 130
7. Bowl, fruit, or small punch, $10\frac{1}{2}$", on standard, sgn'd Libbey — 275
8. Bowl, sq. nappy w/blue center. — 75
9. Bowl, 10" D, footed, one piece, c.1850. Daniel 65C — 450
10. Bowl, punch, on pedestal, 12 cups, 50", Fry. P123 — 10,000
11. Candlesticks, 18", pair, tear drop, all over cutting. — 400
12. Candlesticks, pr., panel cut, tear drop stem, 12"H. Pr. — 300
13. Compote, 12", covered, tear drop stem, well cut. Hawkes. — 275
14. Cruet, vinegar, 7", exc. cutting, signed Hawkes. — 75
15. Cup, punch, 3", Brunswick pattern, P72 — 20
16. Decanter, 9", cut stopper, bulbous w/thin neck. — 100
17. Decanter, 8", flute-cut, ring neck, C.1840. Daniel 58A. — 120
18. Decanter, good cutting and cut stopper, 11". — 100
19. Dish, butter, 6", covered dome & finial, all over cut. — 120
20. Dish, cheese, 8", w/elaborately cut dome and plate. — 175
21. Dish, cheese, Columbia pattern, sgn'd Libbey, Daniel 104 — 175
22. Goblet, 6", fine cutting on bowl, stem & rayed foot. — 40
23. Goblets, 6", Russian pattern, pair. ea. — 75
24. Goblet, Grecian pattern, teardrop stem, but foot, P10. — 75
25. Jar, hair receiver, hobstars. — 50
26. Jar, powder, $3\frac{1}{2}$"D, hobstars. — 80
27. Knife rest, 6", round ends, all over cut — 20
28. Lamp, 23", domed shade, prisms, hobstars. P159-3 — 1000
29. Nappie, 6", w/handle and fine cutting in hobstars — 35
30. Nappie, 10", two handles & divider, heavy close cutting. — 90
31. Nappie, 5", double handle, heavy cutting. — 80
32. Pitcher, 9", tankard shape, hobstars and diamonds. — 100
33. Pitcher, water, 8", Strawberry diamond and star, P8. — 100
34. Pitcher, water, and matching basin. — 135
35. Pitcher, 9", flute-cut, c.1830, Daniel 61A. — 150
36. Plate, 12", extremely fine cutting on thick glass. — 200
37. Plate, 15", intaglio cut fruits, deeply engr., sgn'd Hawkes. — 900
38. Plate, 12", Panel pattern, signed Hawkes, Revi 185. — 275
39. Plate, 12", hobstars, strawberry diam., Daniel 74A. — 250
40. Set, sugar and creamer, fine cutting, mint condition. — 60
41. Set, sugar & creamer, footed, 4", Harvard pattern, P166-5. — 160
42. Set, water pitcher & 6 tumblers, signed Tuthill. — 400
43. Toothpick, strawberry diamond and fan. — 20
44. Tray, $13\frac{1}{2}$ x 9", ice cream, hobstar and fan, P18. — 150
45. Tumbler, 4", Comos pattern with leaves and flower. — 10
46. Tumbler, 4", heavy, all over cut, flared top, sgn'd Hawkes — 25
47. Tumblers, 4", set of six, hobstars, splits and miters. ea. — 16
48. Vase, 10", trumpet shape w/foot, brilliant cutting — 75
49. Vase, 16", loving cup, two handles, sgn'd Libbey, P115 — 500
50. Vase, 12", thin waist, combined cutting and engraving. — 150

200

CUT VELVET GLASS

An acid finish satin glass having a raised pattern most frequently found in diamond quilting. Name derived from the soft dull surface appearance and not from any cutting on the surface. Made by many glass houses in America and probably in Europe. No record of any signed pieces. Scarce.

Grover Plate Number
135 Vase, 11", stick, amethyst diamond quilting, Illus.   250

Other Examples
1. Bowl, 7", ribbed, tan colored   160
2. Tumbler, 3½"H, pink with D.Q. pattern.   160
3. Vase, 8", carafe shaped, blue satin, diamond quilted.   200
4. Vase, 8", double gourd, green satin, diamond quilted.   350
5. Vase, 9", blue with ruffle top, diamond quilted.   240
6. Vase, 6", butterscotch, ribbed.   175

DAUM NANCY GLASS

Probably the second most important maker of fine French Art Glass after Galle who worked in the same city of Nancy in the Northeastern part of France. The Daum factory is still producing contemporary types of engraved, clear and colored crystal glass. While the work of this factory is usually thought of as cameo glass they did use many other techniques such as inlay, gold enameling, and intaglio. A few examples of their work are listed below. For more information and examples refer to the section on French Cameo glass. See Grover's *European Art Glass* for many examples of their outstanding work and detailed information about the history of the company.

775

1. Bowl, French Cameo with pedestal base, 10"D.   425
2. Bowl, sherbet, apricot color flecked w/gold, 4-1/4".   35
3. Goblet, wine, enameled Fr. lily pattern, engr., sgn'd.   170
4. Pitcher, water, flat tortoise shell type, signed.   225
5. Tumbler, wooded snow scene. Signed.   190
6. Vase, petite in three-dimen., cameo decor., 6-3/4".   275
7. Vase, cameo rect. small, signed.   200

DE VILBISS GLASS

This name is listed because collectors encounter atomizers with this name on the bottom. The company manufactures spray equipment, including atomizers. The collectible items with their signature were made from 1900 to 1925 of glass bodies supplied by glass makers such as Steuben, Durand and others. Therefore they are found in the iridescent and other finishes that were popular at that time. Similar atomizers with Steuben signatures are found, Steuben having probably bought the metal portions from DeVilbiss.

40

DeVilbiss

1. Atomizer, gold enamel decoration. 35
2. Atomizer, gold decoration. Signed. 50
3. Atomizer, cranberry color, signed, 6½". 25

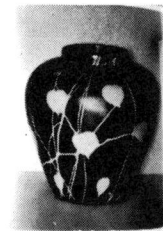

900

DURAND GLASS

Fine colored Art Glass produced by the Durand Art Glass Company of Vineland, N. J. and named after its founder, Victor Durand. Produced glass similar to Tiffany and Steuben but in fewer varieties of kinds and shapes. This company also produced tableware in the distinctive red, blue, and yellow colors with a decoration of white looped threading. Another unusual product of considerable merit was Durand's stretched glass which is also referred to as crackle. Even though these pieces are not signed, they can be safely attributed to Durand because of their unique style and finish. The stretched or crackle glass is a cased glass with the inner layer, often an iridescent blue or gold, and the top layer stretched until the inner layer shows through the crackle or crazed top layer. Signed pieces have large V with name Durand or only name Durand. Threading as an overlay was another Durand specialty but others, especially Steuben used this threading extensively.

Grover Plate Numbers
240 Vase, 9", blue feather on gold lined calcite, threaded. 700
241 Jar, covered, 11", calcite w/pulled gold feathers, sgn'd. 750
242 Vase, 8", blue irid. w/wh. lily pads, signed, illus. 800
243 Vase, 8", gold irid., intaglio cut band, signed. 500
244 Vase, 11", four overlay cut to clear, signed Durand. 570
245 Vase, 10", irid. w/wide marvered threads, signed. 450
246 Jar, covered, 7", red irid., silver marvered threads. 2000
247 Jar, covered, 11", green triple overlay, signed Durand. 1500
248 Vase, 6½", cameo or ACB, blue & black, signed Durand. 950
249 Vase, 10", red crystal, cut & pulled feather, signed. 450
250 Vase, 12", blue irid. & gold crackle, sgn'd V. Durand. 320
251 Vase, 10", red crystal casing cut to clear, signed. 400
252 Bowl, 13", green crystal and white feather. 250
253 Vase, 12", red & white cased glass, signed Durand. 500
254aSherbet, feather pattern on yellow crystal. 100
254bWine, feather pattern on yellow crystal. 125
254cGoblet, feather pattern on yellow crystal. 160

Other Examples
1. Bowl, footed, rose, blue feather decor. 385
2. Compote, candy dish, amethyst, 5½". 175
3. Nappy, ruby gold, Durand. 70
4. Plate, 8", red w/pulled feather design in white. 200
5. Plate, 8", blue/pulled feather design in blue. 175
6. Shade, 10", red with calcite lining, flared. 160
7. Sherbet, cranb. & vaseline candy stripe leaf. Unsigned. 125
8. Vase, black, irid. blue leaf & vine decor., signed. 400

Durand Glass

9. Vase, 8", blown loop, white to green feather pattern. 120
10. Vase, 10", bulbous, blue to gold. 325
11. Vase, cobalt blue iridescent, signed, 10"H. 625
12. Vase, cut glass, cranberry overlay. 400
13. Vase, 7", blue and black decor., signed. 375
14. Vase, flower, reddish gold lustre, irid. blue leaf & vine. 450
15. Vase, irid. gold with trumpet neck, appl. vine decor., $9\frac{1}{2}$". 325
16. Vase, 4"H, golden blue feather pattern. 175
17. Vase, $9\frac{1}{2}$", gold iridescent. 300
18. Vase, 12", on pedestal, trumpet shape, blue irides., sgn'd. 550
19. Vase, pink iridescent, feather stripe pattern. 330
20. Vase, table, cluthra, orange & red, signed. 375
21. Vase, table, 8-3/4", orange gold, silver swag decor. 275
22. Vase, 12", blue lavander. Signed on base. 215
23. Vase, 12", irid. colored peacock feather pattern. 400
24. Vase, $7\frac{1}{2}$", gold iridescent pinched body. 185

ENAMELED GLASS

The range of glass decorated with enamels encompasses hundreds of makers, shapes, styles, colors, as well as many different classifications of art glass and some that are not truly art glass. Usually this decoration is done with a single or multi-colored enamels on colored glass. Sometimes this was done for the decorative effect alone i.e., Mary Gregory Glass and sometimes to simulate or copy finer glass like English Cameo. Because of the broad range of quality and source no attempt is made here to list detailed pieces. For this information see the listing for the specific type of glass such as Albertine, Crown Milano, Royal Flemish, Mary Gregory, and others.

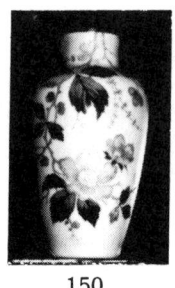  

150   325   50

END-OF-DAY GLASS

This type of glass is more correctly called Spatter Glass which describes it more accurately. It is made up of small splotches of many colors in various sizes so that it looks very much as though it had been spattered with various colors of paints. See the classification Spatter Glass for more details and prices. The story that gaffers took all their leftover bits of colored glass at the end of the day and worked them up into this type is responsible for the name.

FEDERZEICHNUNG GLASS

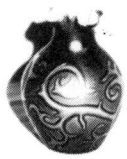

This is the pattern name for one very specialized and rare type of MOTHER OF PEARL satin glass. The design and coloring are distinctive so that once seen is easily remembered if not pronounced. It has been set aside from the general classification to receive more attention.

1400

FENTON GLASS

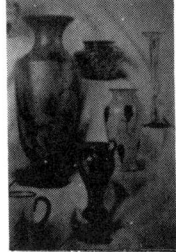

The Fenton family has owned and operated a glass company in West Virginia for almost seventy years. During this time they have made a number of different types of Art Glass which were similar in shape and finish to other companies like Northwood and Imperial and like them also made Carnival Glass. One type of Fenton glass that stands out as different from other makers in the early years of the century had very large splotches of bright colors. It might be termed an oversize Spatter Glass. Unless any Fenton piece is carefully documented or has the original label it is difficult to be sure that it was made by them. At present the Company makes a complete line of Milk Glass that is characterized by a narrow crystal edge. They are again making some pieces of Carnival and have a large line of other color glass items.

75 375

FINDLAY GLASS (ONYX)

Glass referred to by this name is also known as Onyx. It is frequently called by either or both names. It was a product of a glass maker located in Findlay, Ohio. For further details and examples see the classification Onyx. Made mostly for tableware by pressing, it is now scarce and high priced.

700

FIREGLOW GLASS

Very few pieces of this little known and under-researched glass are found. The ones given this name have a tan or ecru satin finish which is usually decorated with fine enamel flowers or birds in blacks and browns. This glass has been attributed to the Boston & Sandwich Glass Company. It is still modestly priced when compared to the better documented Burmese and Peachblow, especially so when considering its very limited availability.

150

Grover Plate Numbers
134 Jar, covered rose $5\frac{1}{2}$"D, decorated with birds.   180
135 Vase, stick, $9\frac{1}{2}$"H, prunus & bird design.   140

Other Examples
1. Bowl, rose, 5"D, enamel decor. in brown & black.   160
2. Ewer, 7½", decorated with ruffled top.   150
3. Vase, bulbous, in tan w/colored flowers, 8".   125

FRANCESWARE GLASS

One of the family of hobnail glassware that was made in many patterns, shapes, and finishes. Francesware as it was called by Hobbs, Brockunier & Co. of Wheeling, West Virginia, who first made it, was always given an acid matte finish except for the crimped band at the top of the piece. This was left clear and then stained amber. Thus the other name for this ware is Frosted Hobnail with Amber Band. This is one of the pattern wares that was at some times pressed and other times mold blown. For this reason, it is sometimes classified with pattern glass. However, this glass is becoming more sought after by collectors and is now often associated with Art Glass at show and ales.

45

1. Bon-Bon, covered, 6", with amber finial.   100
2. Bowl, 8", four sided, some slight imperfections.   75
3. Creamer, frosted handle, ground pontil.   45
4. Pitcher, water, 8", slight imperfections on hobs.   175
5. Shade, 9"D, dome shaped   125
6. Sugar, 4", frosted handles, ground pontil.   40
7. Toothpick, 2", small hob, ground pontil.   60
8. Tray, 14"D, for water set, clover shaped.   125
9. Tumbler, 4", mint condition with ground pontil.   35
10. Vase, celery, 6", good condition.   60

FRY GLASS

One type of glass made by the H. C. Fry Co. of Rochester, Pennsylvania. This was actually called Foval when it was introduced. This company was probably better known at that time for the high quality cut glass they produced during the Brilliant Period. The glass now called Fry is opalescent in the main part and has attachments or applications of one or more other colors. These are predominately blues and greens. The combination is quite striking and sometimes confused with the Steuben Jades that were produced by Carder. This glass has received much more attention from collectors in the past few years, and prices have responded accordingly. Not many of these pieces are found signed or marked but like other distinctive types, many of the pieces can be safely attributed to Fry because of the particular shape or color combination. This does not apply to the tableware produced by this firm, as very similar wares were produced by other unknown firms and may at times be represented as Fry. See color illustration #9 on front cover.

175

Grover Plate Numbers
419 Pitcher, 8", blue/white opal, amethyst handle.   200
420 Candlesticks, 12", pair white opal, blue and green.   260
421 Pot, coffee, covered, white opal, blue handle & finial. 250

Fry Glass - Other Examples - cont'd
1. Bowl, 12", centerpiece on green base & opalescent body   175
2. Bowl, 10"D, white with blue trim.   150
3. Candlesticks, 10", opal white body w/blue threading. pr.   250
4. Compote, 7", opalescent white w/blue threading.   175
5. Compote, 10", folded gr. edge, opal. stripes, irid. cl. glass   80
6. Creamer, 5", tankard shape white opal. body w/bl. handle.   100
7. Cup and Saucer, cup white opal w/blue handle.   60
8. Cup and Saucer, $5\frac{1}{2}$" across saucer.   75
9. Pitcher, water, green stripe w/blue applied handle.   185
10. Shade, light, cranberry opaline, $4\frac{1}{2}$".   30
11. Vase, 8", signed Fry, white opal. w/lavender top.   120
12. Vase, 10", trumpet shaped w/blue foot and opal. body. Illus.   120

GALLE GLASS

This glass is named after Emile Galle who is credited as one of the originators of the Art Nouveau movement and probably did more than any other one person that worked in glass to make this movement the outstanding success that it was. Much of his work falls in the category of French Cameo, which see. However, as a creative genius he produced many other types and designs. For further details see Grover's *European Art Glass* and Blount's *French Cameo Glass*.

2500

1. Bowl, hand painted enamel, branch & leaf design, sgn'd.   130
2. Bowl, on pedestal, $8\frac{1}{2}$"D, signed.   275
3. Goblet, champagne, etched & decorated, signed, 5-1/4"   160
4. Lamp, table, pastel yellow ground, orange leaves, sgn'd.   650
5. Medallion, profile of Napoleon, $3\frac{1}{2}$"D.   125
6. Tumbler, painted thick enamel decor. Signed. W-p24   100
7. Tumbler, hand painted enamel arabesques, signed, $4\frac{1}{2}$".   125
8. Vase, faience, cabbage shape, signed, 5".   180
9. Vase, petite, light & dark mauve, signed, 8".   170
10. Vase, baluster shape, clear to red frosted ground, sgn'd.   300
11. Vase, purple iris design, hand wheel ground, sgn'd. W-p24   120
12. Vase, ceramic decorated, $9\frac{1}{2}$". W-p24   250
13. Vase, $2\frac{1}{2}$"D, floral & multicolor, signed.   130
14. Vase, 2"H, with pine cone decoration. Signed.   125

GREEN OPAQUE GLASS

A very scarce product of the New England Glass Co. and belonging to the satin glass family but made in a very distinctive shade of soft green with a mottled decoration around the top of each piece. This decoration was produced by a further application of stain after the opaque glass had been acid treated to give the soft finish. The mottled decoration was normally separated from the main body by a narrow band of gold which outlined the wavy edge of the decoration.

750

Grover Plate Numbers   Green Opaque
96. Bowl, 3", open top and wide band of decoration.   500
97. Creamer, 4", fine band of decoration and gold trim.   600
98. Cruet, Vinegar, 5", design covers complete neck.   750

Other Examples
1. Cup, punch, with handle, good color   400
2. Tumbler, 4", water, stain and gold in mint condition.   350
3. Tumbler, 4", water, with small repair   100
4. Vase, 6", celery with rare added enamel decoration.   600

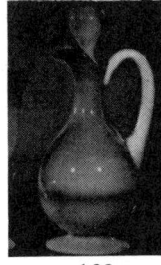

GUNDERSON GLASS

The Gunderson Glass Company which traces its history back through the Pairpont Company to the Mt. Washington Glass Company, not too long ago made reproductions of two types of glass originally produced by the predecessor company. These were Burmese and Peachblow. At the time of their introduction they were considered and priced as reproductions of the original ware which they resembled quite closely. Today they are commanding premium prices far in excess of the initial selling price but not yet at the level that the original products sell for. Both types of reproductions are not as colorful as the original ware, and the glass itself is somewhat heavier in appearance. The fact that colors are rather weak makes it possible for any collector to tell the difference without too much difficulty. Some of the types produced are listed and priced below. These can be compared to the original ware by referring to the proper category.

160

1. Bowl, 7", with curled feet, Burmese color   125
2. Creamer, 4", New England PB color   125
3. Cruet, vinegar, Mt. Washington PB color   160
4. Cup and saucer, 3", fairly good Mt. Washington PB color.   200
5. Cup and saucer, New England PB type.   150
6. Cup and saucer, New England PB type.   160
7. Cup, punch, Mt. Washington PB color.   100
8. Hat, small, 3", Mt. Washington PB color.   90
9. Lamp, fairy, w/crimped top and plate, Burmese color.   240
10. Lamp, miniature, Burmese coloring   100
11. Sugar bowl, 4", New England PB color.   120
12. Tumbler, water, 4", Mt. Washington PB color.   130
13. Tumbler, water, 4", shiny Burmese color.   95
14. Tumbler, 4", dull finish Burmese.   85
15. Tumbler, New England PB type.   110
16. Vase, 3", w/applied prunts, Mt. Washington PB color.   150
17. Vase, 12", trumpet shaped, rose to wh., N.E. PB type.   300
18. Vase, Burmese, footed, decorated.   170

225

HANDEL GLASS

While better known for its lamps the Handel Company also made other decorative articles such as vases and jars using some of techniques employed for lamps. One common characteristic is the rough textured finish of the glass surface which was accomplished by using a glue solution that actually removed some of the glass surface. This is in contrast to the acid etching surface preparation used by many other firms.

Lamps which were the mainstay of the company and for which they are remembered today were produced late in the 19th and early 20th century. While many styles of lamps were produced apparently the textured surface dome shades with scenes hand painted on the inside are those encountered most frequently today. They also made bent glass shades and some examples of their leaded shades could easily be confused with similar Tiffany items.

As with all well done and popular items, other producers made very similar items and unless the lamp or other article is signed Handel or still has the original label it is difficult to attribute the work to this firm.

Fine artistic examples of their lamps have greatly appreciated in price over the past few years and seem destined to continue upwards at a rapid pace.

1. Bowl, textured surface w/H.P. design of trees, signed, 8". 75
2. Jar, tobacco, white with H.P. flowers, signed, 6". 85
3. Lamp, desk with "U" frame & H.P. shade in woodland scene.125
4. Lamp, G.W.W. style globe on tall metal base. Signed. 175
5. Lamp, table, w/forest scene painted on inside, signed. 300
6. Lamp, table w/large floral design on inside, signed. 400
7. Lamp, table w/leaded shade in form of colored flowers.sgn'd 500
8. Lamp, table in form of bent glass lily w/bronze base. 225

750

HOLLY AMBER GLASS

This mold-pressed glass has enjoyed remarkable acceptance by collectors. This is probably due to the fact that among the pressed molded ware that is so common in clear glass, this has a very distinctive color combination of alternating translucent bands of a rich amber and white opolescent glass. The amber portions are impressed with stylized holly leaves. The white opal portion is especially effective because of the varying pearl-like irregularity. A second reason is the fact that while this product was well received, there was not enough of it made to satisfy the many ambitious collectors who are searching for good examples today. It has been reported that reproductions of some pieces have been seen.

Grover Plate Numbers
416 Compote, covered, 9", fair coloring, light amber. 750
417 Jug, syrup, 6", pewter top, good colors. 400
418 Dish, butter, $5\frac{1}{2}$", covered, excellent colors. 1200

Other Examples   Holly Amber

1. Bowl, berry, oak leaf & hob nail pattern, 8½".	400
2. Bowl, open sugar.	350
3. Bowl, oval on pedestal, 7½" W. W-p1	275
4. Butter dish, with matching lid. W-p1	1250
5. Compote, jelly with cover, 6-1/4".	450
6. Compote, covered, 12½". W-p1	1200
7. Compote, covered jelly.	625
8. Creamer, 3"H.	350
9. Cup, with handle, 5".	250
10. Dish, covered candy, dark color, dolphin, 7".	450
11. Dish, relish, oblong, 7½".	275
12. Dish, covered candy, on pedestal, 8".	375
13. Dish, oval relish.	225
14. Dish, relish, oval, 7½".	350
15. Dish, sauce.	155
16. Parfait, footed.	350
17. Pitcher, cream, 4".	400
18. Pitcher, syrup with pewter lid, 6".	400
19. Pitcher & tumblers, rare set of 7 pieces, W-p1	2250
20. Plate, round, 9-1/4".	1300
21. Plate, round cake on pedestal stand, rare, 9-1/4".	850
22. Plate, square, 7½". W-p1	250
23. Set, condiment, serpentine shaped tray on 4. W-p1	750
24. Set, spoon holder, c'v'd sugar bowl, creamer, c'v'd butter.	2000
25. Toothpick, rare pedestal base, 5". W-p1	375
26. Toothpick, 2-1/4"H.	200
27. Toothpick, holder, 2½".	250
28. Tumbler, water, 3½"H.	285
29. Vase, small table, 6", footed.	350

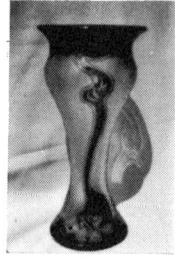

275

HONESDALE GLASS

A very scarce type of cameo (acid cutback) Art Glass that to date has received very little notice. This glass was produced on blanks made by the Dorflinger Glass Company which produced the finest cut glass in Honesdale, Pa. The original company was a joint venture of the Dorflingers and Carl Prosch, a noted decorator from Austria. It was named the Honesdale Decorating Company and should not be confused with an earlier Honesdale Glass Co. While fine gold decorated tablewares were produced by this company, their best known and most artistic work was in the form of fine multicolored cameo vases. The blanks used were crystal cased with a transparent green, yellow, or red. The design was etcher in with acid leaving the pattern in relief and the crystal in a textured matte surface. The finer designs also included other colors applied as stains. Many of the artistic pieces are signed with the word "Honesdale" in gold slanted script. Pieces listed below are all signed Honesdale except the goblet which was done on a blank marked "H" (for Heisey).

Honesdale

1. Bowl, 8"D, heavy cameo design in green scrolls   160
2. Goblet, 7", embossed gold border, gold design,Heisey blank   35
3. Vase, rare 10" green & gold cameo, signed.   175
4. Vase, Honesdale, morning glory design, $5\frac{1}{2}$".   275
5. Vase, 12", green cameo cattails & wild geese outlined gold.   400
6. Vase, 12", yellow cameo flowers, gold edging.   300
7. Vase, 9" bulbous, green cameo scrolls, gold decoration.   200
8. Vase, 12", acid finish w/wh. enamel scrolls, green beads.   260
9. Vase, 7", flared top, yellow cameo mums outlined in gold.   175
10. Vase, 4", yellow cameo scrolls, on iridescent crystal   225
11. Vase, 10", cameo yellow crystal outlined in gold.   200

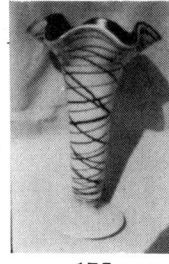

175

IMPERIAL GLASS

As glass companies go Imperial is an old timer, having been in continuous production since about 1900 in Bellaire, Ohio. During these seventy odd years they have made a great many different types of glass. It is not unlikely that this variety was responsible for its survival during the Great Depression when most others were collapsing right and left. Much of the production was in inexpensive pressed glass. As a result the Company is probably best known for its iridescent Carnival Glass made during the early years of the century.

Since this was very inexpensive ware produced as giveaway premiums it is amazing to see the hundred of dollars being paid today for some examples. At the same time fine high quality examples of Imperial's scarce Art Glass brings only a fraction of these lofty prices.

This fine hand blown glass which they called Free Hand is the equivalent of Tiffany, Steuben or Durand, in design or composition. In fact Emil Larson the great glass maker from Durand is responsible for some of this work. However today's prices do not reflect such equality. Since there is less of this glass than the better known ones the answer must lie in the demand and not the supply. It is quite likely that this disparity will vanish in the years to come as the merit of fine Imperial glass is fully appreciated and recognized.

1. Bowl, gold iridescent, four sided, 5"D.   50
2. Bowl, rimmed, 13"D, irid. stretch blue.   100
3. Bowl, shallow, iridized blue milk glass.   50
4. Bowl, ribbed amberiam, signed, 9"D.   90
5. Bowl, stretched iridescent blue, paneled, signed.   45
6. Candlesticks, 10"H, crystal w/red cups & bases.   pr.   35
7. Pitcher, blue hob nail, $8\frac{1}{2}$".   45
8. Shade, light, $2\frac{1}{2}$"D, Nuart in zig-zag iridescent.   20
9. Vase, ruffled edge, red, signed, 6".   35
10. Vase, gold iridescent, 6".   70
11. Vase, $9\frac{1}{2}$"H, opal body with blue irid. leaf & vine.   20
12. Vase, 12", gold and blue leaves entwined, unsigned.   125
13. Vase, 10", free hand blue irides., wh. leaves & vines. Illus.   150

KELVA GLASS

One of three named products of the C. F. Monroe Company of Meriden, Connecticut. All three products are similar in appearance having high-grade enamel decoration on opaque opal glass blanks that this firm may have purchased from a number of different sources. Most of the items seen today were made to serve useful purposes and yet were artistic in nature and extremely well done by high-grade artists. Most examples appear to have been designed for the bedroom and boudoir, such as hair receivers, cuff and collar boxes, powder jars, and other types of covered pieces. Because of the quality of the work and limited number of pieces available, prices have advanced rapidly in the past few years. For examples of this same maker under names Nakara & Wavecrest, refer to these two classifications.

375

Kelva - Grover Plate No.
113 Box, 5½", cover, with clock, blue floral, name. Illus.   375

Other Examples

1. Box, powder, 8", hexagonal, pink & white, signed.   130
2. Box, powder, footed w/clock in top, floral panels   280
3. Box, dresser, unsigned, good decoration   100
4. Humidor, tobacco, tan w/floral design, 6"H.   250
5. Jar, dark blue, white panel, "Cigars", 6"H.   320
6. Receiver, hair, 4", little decoration, signed.   80

KEW BLAS GLASS

W. S. Blake, superintendent, of the Union Glass Company in Somerville, Massachusetts, is credited with naming this Art Glass product by rearranging the letters in his name until they formed a suitable trade name. Since many of the glass workers and designers in this period worked in more than one factory, there is a definite similarity between this glass and contemporary production of other shops such as Steuben, Tiffany, Durand, and Quezel. Like other types, Kew Blas pieces are also seen without signatures. Comparison with the same or very similar articles is one way of making attribution. Thorough documentation is another way in which unsigned pieces produced during the Art Nouveau Period can be definitely identified as the product of one of the above-named shops.

500

Grover Plate Numbers
235 Vase, 6", calcite w/gold inside, wavy gold decoration.   300
236 Vase, 9", calcite, gold & green feather design, signed.   475
237 Vase, 6", calcite, gold, overlay and feather decor., sgn'd   550
238 Vase, 4", calcite, gold w/gr. & gold feather, sgn'd. Illus.   500

Other Examples   Kew Blas
1. Candlestick, 9", calcite & gold w/green feather, unsigned.   175
2. Compote, 6", gold iridescent, unsigned   200
3. Compote, 4", low footed, gold irides. w/loops, signed   375
4. Tumbler, 4", gold with feather decoration.   220
5. Vase, 8", cylindrical calcite & gold w/feather design, sgn'd   300
6. Vase, 8", dark blue irides., white looped decor., signed.   650
7. Vase, 12", iridescent, cat tail pattern.   200
8. Vase, MOP w/green/gold feather design, signed.   300

KIMBALL GLASS

A classification of Art Glass made in limited designs and quantities by the Kimball Glass Company of Vineland, New Jersey, where Durand Glass was also made. There is evidence that at one time these two companies were associated in a business relationship, as pieces signed "Durand-Kimball" are infrequently seen. (see below). The Kimball firm is best known in this field for a type of cluthra glass they produced. Some collectors confuse it with Steuben Cluthra. However, the two are quite different in shape, color, and in the "Cluthra" effect if they are studied side by side. The Kimball pieces do not seem so appealing as the Steuben pieces. Kimball also produced commercial glass in the form of vials and other small glass containers.

250

Grover Plate Numbers
257 Vase, 5", blue cluthra design, signed Kimball.   250
258 Vase, 8", two-colored cluthra, sgn'd Kimball. Illus.   300

Other Examples
1. Vases, pair, decorated fireglo, signed, $10\frac{1}{2}$".   pr.   675
2. Vase, crystal, green to white w/enamel, sgn'd, 10".   80
3. Vase, Durand cluthra, deep emerald green.   250
4. Vase, cluthra, reddish gold to light yellow.   250
5. Vase, 12", white w/enamel, signed Durand-Kimball   240
6. Vase, 10", cluthra type, signed Kimball   210
7. Vase, 8", stick necked green w/white markings, sgn'd.   100

KLONDIKE

A distinctive pattern glass with satin finish and crossed bands that are stained amber. It was made by at least two firms which may account for the two different names for the same pattern. Probably better known by the name of Amberette, a number of similar examples are shown in this earlier section. Because of its scarcity and unusual design it is infrequently offered for sale where more conventional Art Glass items are sold.

125

Klondike

1. Dish, butter, covered, square. 125
2. Dish, sauce, frosted and stained, 4" 50
3. Set, creamer and sugar, covered bowl 175
4. Pitcher, water, 8", frosted and stained 125
5. Tumbler, water, 4", frosted and stained 75
6. Toothpick, rare, 2"H, mint condition. 150

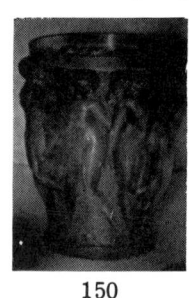

LALIQUE GLASS

First made by Rene Lalique in the latter part of the Nineteenth Century and still carried on in France by members of his family to the present day. Originally Lalique made single pieces of art glass in the true cameo technique. As demand increased, he began to mold glass items in larger quantities of very high quality. These were finished in acid to give a matte, silky surface. Lalique is still produced in various forms of artistic glass today. The inability to distinguish between older pieces and those produced today may be a factor in the lack of appreciation of this glass by collectors so far. Almost all work is signed with an incised diamond point script signature, or molded in embossed form. A recent innovation was a limited edition Annual Plate in clear crystal with a matte pressed design, dated 1965. This design of two herons was created by his daughter Marie-Claude as was the 1966 plate entitled Dreamrose.

150

1. Vase, 7", frosted spherical shape, antelope designs, signed $ 70
2. Vase, 7", frosted with design of nesting birds 80
3. Dish, 4", covered with impressed birds 60
4. Figure, fish, 5", in clear polished crystal 35
5. Candlesticks, 6", pair, elaborate embossed designs, signed 220

LEGRAS GLASS

One of the typical French contemporaries of Gallé in the manufacture of cameo glass in colorful floral and scenic views. Unless signed they are practically indistingishable from other makers. Fortunately this is seldom a problem since most makers of the French Cameo type glass had their name etched in the glass along with the design. See classification Cameo Glass, French for further information and examples with prices.

175

LIBBEY GLASS

The name Libbey was first associated with the production of fine artistic American glass more than one hundred years ago, in the management of such famous firms as the Mt. Washington Glass Company and the New England Glass Company. When this latter firm had a serious strike that permanently closed the plant, the Libbeys moved to Toledo, Ohio, where they formed the Libbey Glass Company which became one of the best known names in the production of very fine and

250

38

Libbey

elaborate pieces of cut glass from 1890 until the early years of this century. The firm is still in the business of producing commercial glass. Most of the glass produced under Libbey management is associated with the names that were used in the patent papers such as Amberina, Pomona, and others developed by Joseph Locke while employed there. A few pieces of some cut glass bear the Libbey script signature in addition to those reintroduced pieces of Amberina made around 1920 (for a color illustration see #2 on front cover). Others are a combination of their fine cut and colored glass.

Grover Plate Numbers
404 Bowl, 2½", cream colored satin, decorated, signed	450
405 Tazza, 6", crystal and shades of blue, signed. Illus.	400
406 Candlestick, 6", crystal stem, red feather top, signed.	420

Other Examples
1. Basket, 7", cut glass with florals and geometrics, sgn'd.	200
2. Bowl, berry, 9"D, cut in heavy glass, signed.	100
3. Goblet, wine, kangaroo stem, signed, 6".	60
4. Punch bowl, cut, on cut pedestal, 12"D, hobstar & splits	475
5. Salt, decorated, signed.	100
6. Toothpick, 2"H, decorated and signed.	65
7. Toothpick, 2"H, decorated and signed.	95
8. Vase, 12", corset shaped, amethyst overlay cut to clear	275
9. Vase, 10", amberina Jack-in-Pulpit, signed Libbey	275
10. Vase, 16", loving cup w/two handles, footed, signed.	375

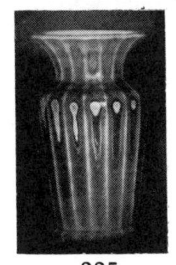

LITHYALIN GLASS

225

This opaque dense glass was developed in Bohemia (now Czechoslovakia) by one of the great glass artists of the time by the name of Eggermann. His object was to reproduce the beauty of polished semi-precious stone such as agate. This ware was produced over one hundred years ago and has a characteristic gray-green lining. Other attempts at the production of agate or stone glass has been made before and since and should not be confused with this highly individual work.

Grover Plate Numbers
383 Bowl, 3", brown and cream polished panels.	175
384 Vase, 15", cut panels in various shades.	225
385 Vase, 9", footed eight-sided in mahogany brown.	300

LOCKE GLASS

775

Sometime around 1900 Joseph Locke left the employ of the Libbey Glass Company and moved to Pittsburgh, Pennsylvania, where for about thirty years he produced and sold a limited quantity of decorated glass which was signed "Locke" or "Locke Art." During this period period he executed fine examples of etched glass, as distinguished from the usual engraving, on clear crystal blanks purchased from local glass companies to his specifications. Any such pieces are highly sought after

Locke (Cont'd.)
by collectors and many of his finer pieces are already in museums. One of the most famous glass inventors and designers, he first worked in England where he established an enviable reputation as a designer and engraver of hand-carved cameo glass. When he came to America about 1890, he worked for the New England Glass Company where he invented such outstanding types of glass as Amberina, Agata, and Pomona, before moving to Toledo. During earlier years he may have also signed some of his fine hand cameo pieces in England.

Grover Nos.
423 Pitcher, $13\frac{1}{2}$", clear crystal etched in vintage patt. signed   750

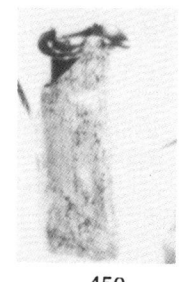

LOETZ GLASS

Loetz Glass is the product of a famous factory of that name which operated in the Western part of Austria known as the Bohemian Woods. They had a world-wide reputation for high-quality glassware and during the Art Nouveau Period they became well known for their beautiful iridescent glass which was similar to the work of Tiffany and Carder of Steuben. Unfortunately, not much of the production was signed with the name. A great deal of inferior iridescent glass is attributed to Loetz without justification. Especially noteworthy is dark blue iridescent with splashes of silver-blue iridescent overlaying the darker one a sillustrated in Revis 19th Century Glass page 231 and also shown here.

450

Grover Plate Numbers
392 Vase, 6", purple-silver irides., signed Loetz.   175
393 Vase, $4\frac{1}{2}$", expanded silver-blue irides., signed.   275
394 Vase, 5", expanded gold irides., signed Loetz.   150
395 Vase, 6", blue-gold irid., lily pads, signed Loetz.   250
396 Vase, $12\frac{1}{2}$", flower form, signed Loetz.   240
397 Vase, 12", gold irid. w/tubular application.   320

Other Examples
1. Basket, brides, red w/enamel decor., silver holder   375
2. Bottle, barber, iridescent blue, unsigned.   120
3. Bowl, 12"D, gold irides. w/applied glass.   225
4. Bowl, shallow, ruffled edge, pearly opal.w/marble purple.   210
5. Candlestick, 10", red and green fern decoration.   140
6. Epergne, four green trumpet lillies & small baskets   275
7. Jar, 8"D, cameo floral design, signed   240
8. Toothpick, miniature, silver overlay, unsigned.   100
9. Vase, 19"H, peacock blue & silver irides., unsigned. Illus.   450
10. Vase, art nouveau w/bronze female figure holding vase.   160
11. Vase, unmarked art nouveau, $9\frac{1}{2}$".   80
12. Vase, 8", bronze irides., pedestal base, unsigned.   90
13. Vase, 10", fine iridescence w/heavy silver overlay, sgn'd.   240
14. Vase, MOP, gold swag decoration, signed.   300
15. Vase, flower, European w/sterling filigree work.unsgn'd.   200
16. Vase, removable silver rim, signed. 6"   W-p36   300

Loetz - cont'd

17. Vase, 8", green iridescent, unsigned		75
18. Vase, 6", green iridescent, unsigned. (Loetz ?)		22
19. Vase, 12", dark & light blue irides., Revi 231		380
20. Vase, 12½", bluish green.		100
21. Vase, 6", blue iridescent pinched sides.		280
22. Vase, 7", feather design, blue irides., signed Loetz		300
23. Vase, flower in bronze stand, lotus leaf pattern.		300
24. Vase, 6", gold iridescent, signed Loetz.		160
25. Vase, 10", flower form, applied leaf on stem.		250

LUTZ GLASS

Nicholas Lutz was a French glassworker who came to this country in the middle of the 19th Century and worked for a number of American firms including the Boston & Sandwich Glass Company. During this period, filigree, striped, threaded, and so-called cane glass were very popular. Somehow the habit arose of calling anything of this nature Lutz glass because he is thought to have been instrumental in its production at Sandwich. Very little of this type of glass can be traced directly to having been made at Sandwich at the time Lutz was there. If this cannot be done with certainty, it is preferable ot refer to any of this kind of glass as Lutz Type Glass. This is especially true since it was more or less an adaptation of techniques ued by Venetian glassmakers for centuries and still being produced on the island of Murano in Venice to this day. (See p#101 of 19th Century Glass by Revi for illustration.)

300

1. Bowl, and under plate, gold speckled & stripped.   70
2. Bowl, finger and plate, red & white filigree striping.   60
3. Cup and saucer, 4", filigree white and light blue.   40-120
4. Goblet, threaded, stemmed, applied rosettes.   60
5. Jar, 14", covered, applied decoration, footed, attrib. Lutz   750
6. Set, washbowl & pitcher, Wheeling type, some history.   425
7. Tumbler, water, 4", twisted blue & white latticine   50
8. Vase, 12", white and applied bosses, filigree handles.   275
9. Wine, threaded and footed.   50

MAIZE GLASS

This is actually decorated milk glass simulating ears of corn. It was produced by the Libbey Glass Company of Toledo, Ohio, about 1890 under the name "Maize Art Glass" which may account for its inclusion in some Art Glass classifications. This should more properly be classified under Milk Glass because of inherent qualities and the quantities in which it was produced. Speculation and scarcity may be other reasons why it sometimes appears under Art Glass.

75

Grover Plate Numbers
422 Vase, celery, 7", white with green husks.   70

Other Examples
1. Bowl, berry, 8", white decorated with green husks   50
2. Creamer, 3", white with green husks   75
3. Dish, butter, covered, white with green husks.   100
4. Pitcher, water, 8", white with green husks   140
5. Sugar bowl, 3", white with green husks   65
6. Toothpick, 2", white with green husks.   125
7. Tumbler, water, 4", white with green husks.   50

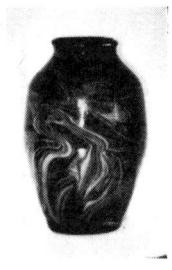

MARBLE GLASS

A multi-colored mixture of glass of several different colors to simulate natural quarry marble stone characterized by random sweeping striations. The old large glass marbles are probably the commonest form of this glass. Other similar glasses made to represent other stone or gem formations are sometimes lumped into this classification, i.e., Agate, Lithyalin or Slag Glass. Each of these is described in other sections.

1800

MARY GREGORY GLASS

Named for a decorator who is supposed to have worked for the Boston & Sandwich Glass Company on Cape Cod. The glass is either clear or colored transparent crystal on which are depicted in white enamel either a young boy or a young girl, frequently chasing butterflies. Other subjects are found. inasmuch as this glass was known to have been produced in England, Czechoslovakia, and Venice, there is very little likelihood of a given piece having been produced at the Boston & Sandwich Glass Company, let alone by Mary Gregory herself. In fact, this glass is still commercially made in Czechoslovakia and in Venice. Probably experts can distinguish certain characteristics that assure its age and authenticity, but for the average collector this is a good area to leave strictly to those few experts. To most people there are many other fields in American Art Glass that are much more representative of the fine artistic workmanship than these simple enameled pieces which at times are far overpriced.

100

Grover Numbers
128 Vase, 8", green with rigaree & enamel decor. Illus.   100
129 Vase, 8", Rubina Verde w/white enamel decoration.   140

Other Examples
1. Bottle, perfume, with stopper, electric blue.   185
2. Box, snuff, black glass.   90
3. Decanter, liquor, elec. blue, original stopper, 9". W-p6   80
4. Epergne, elec.blue, ruffled edge, 14-3/4". W-p6   375
5. Mug, milk, $3\frac{1}{2}$", blue with enamel decoration.   35
6. Mug, beer, 5", handled, amber w/white decoration.   50
7. Pitchers, pair in blue w/male & female figures. W-p6 pr. 225
8. Pitcher, ewer type, emerald green, classic enamel W-p6   120

Mary Gregory

9.	Pitcher, cream, 6", green with reeded handle	60
10.	Pitcher, water, 8", clear w/white enamel decor.	75
11.	Set, night, elec. blue:bottle, tumbler, under dish. W-p6	200
12.	Tumbler, electric blue, with girl figure.	35
13.	Tumbler, clear glass, boy with net. W-p6	25
14.	Tumbler, 3"H, smoked, girl in white.	110
15.	Vase, cranberry, 4", girl in white. W-p6	100
16.	Vase, emerald green, clear glass trim.	60

MILLEFIORE GLASS

A very ancient technique for producing glass articles that have random multicolored glass discs imbedded in the surface to give a mosiac effect. (See color illustration #13 on Front Cover.) The term means "thousand flowers" and that is exactly what a finished piece of this type looks like, since each little disc was made to resemble a flower. The discs were obtained by slicing multi-colored glass rods in thin sections. The glass rods were made by making a bundle of smaller rods in different colors so that in looking at the end of the bundle a varigated design was produced depending on the arrangement of the rods. When the bundle was fired, the rods all fused into one mass which could be drawn into great lengths without changing the cross-section arrangement. Each little disc sliced from the end of the rod was an exact replica of the previous one. The Venetians re-developed this art to a high degree in the Middle Ages and are still using it to produce replicas of older pieces as well as experimenting in using them in more modern applications. One of the leaders in this work is the firm of Barovier & Toso on the Island of Murano offshore from Venice. Dr. Angelo Barovier whose family has been in the glass business on Murano since about 1350 is a brilliant creative artist, developing new techniques in using glass as an art form. This technique was used on a few American pieces such as Carder's "Tessera".

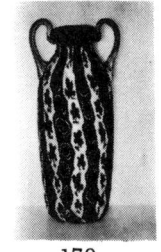

170

Grover Plate Numbers

379	Vase, unusual dragonfly design w/netting, signed.	400
380	Pitcher, cream, 4", scattered millefiore on wh. ground.	100
381	Vase, 8", double handle laid millefiore in rows. Illus.	175
382	Vase, 8", random millefiore on blue background.	325

Other Examples

1.	Cruet, 5", all millefiore including handle & stopper.	175
2.	Dish, 6"D, in brass holder. Various colors.	100
3.	Lamp, 7", miniature w/dome shade & base in millefiore	120
4.	Lamp, 10", w/shade, both in lavendar canes. W-p29	140
5.	Paperweight, 3", crowned allover design, modern	15
6.	Tumbler, 4", overall millefiore in blues and greens	75
7.	Tumbler, $3\frac{1}{2}$"H, varied colors. W-p35	60
8.	Vase, miniature, 4"H, blue.	70
9.	Vase, purple, ruffled top.	70
10.	Vase, 8", double handled on lav. background (Venetian)	75

MOSER GLASS

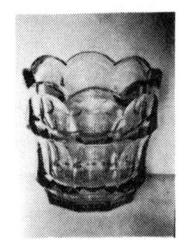

125

Glass made by the Moser Glass Works in Carlsbad which is now Karlovy-Vary in Czechoslovakia where this firm just recently celebrated its hundredth anniversary and is still producing fine artistic glass as well as their famous tableware services for crowned heads and other important persons all over the world. This glassworks was started in the late 1850's by Leo Moser, a well-known artist and glass engraver, who was doing commission portrait work on glass for important patrons of this famous spa. One of their principal products has been the typical beautigully engraved pieces done with the copper wheel on clear crystal, and on this clear crystal a color was cased so that the finished design was framed by the color when the design was cut through. They have for years made other fine pieces in artistic forms that were only cut and polished. One of their well-known products is the orchid colored glass which they call Alexandrite.

Grover Plate Numbers
389 Bowl, 5", cut panels, sgn'd Moser-Alexandrite.   125
390 Vase, 10", handled, overall enamelled, signed.   320

Other Examples
1. Bottle, w/stopper, fine cut green to white, signed.   65
2. Bottle, perfume, cobalt blue, gold decorated figures, $4\frac{1}{2}$".   65
3. Bowl, prismatic, amethyst to clear, engr. decor., signed.   400
4. Candlesticks, pair, amethyst crystal, 4", signed. W-p8. pr   70
5. Compote, blue & clear floral decor. w/gold trim.   70
6. Cruet, vinegar, 5", petticoat style.   200
7. Epergne, w/metal mount, amber, enamel decor. sgn'd Moser   300
8. Pitcher, water, heavy enamel decor., unsgn'd. W-p6   250
9. Vase, small, footed, pure gold & enamel decor., signed.   100
10. Vase, miniature, amethyst, painted decor., $3\frac{1}{2}$".   75
11. Vase, amber & blue, enamel flowers, 7".   400

MOTHER-OF-PEARL SATIN GLASS

260

A double layered opaque colored satin glass article which by several different techniques had a design created under the outer surface. See #14 on front cover for a color illustration. The result is on a pearly luster effect against the dull satin finish of the rest of the article. Patterns in this ware are Diamond Quilted (abbreviated in most literature to DQ), Moire, Raindrop, and Herringbone. The so-caller air traps that produced the pearly effect were made by indenting the first basic layer of glass in the desired outline and then casing it with a color coating that left air in the indented areas to show through the outer layer in a pearl-like luster. This glass was extremely popular during the Victorian Period and was made in America, England, and several European countries. The vast majority of the pieces was not signed, so that this glass is collected solely for its desirability rather than for the factory which made it. The most desirable coloring is Rainbow, which see.

Mother of Pearl - Grover Numbers

17. Ewer. w/swirl pattern, shaded rose, 12". 250
18. Vase, ribbed, zipper pattern, chartreuse lining, 16". 275
19. Vase, thorn handles, heringbone design, shaded rose. 240
20. Basket, thorn handle, moire pattern, enamel decor., 12" 375
21. Vase, raindrop design, decor., shaded apricot, 11". 260
22. Vase, peacock eye design, enamel decor., white, 8". 300
24. Vase, 10", green MOP Federzeichung design. 900
25. Vase, 6", brown w/Federzeichung design. 1250
26. Vase, 12", orchid D.Q. w/enamel decoration. 300
27. Vase, $13\frac{1}{2}$", MOP swirl with gold enamel. 300
28. Vase, 7", shaded rose, D.Q. (Webb?) 275
29. Vase, 10", hand, blue MOP 250
30. Vase, 9", footed, beige MOP, zipper pattern. 350

Other Examples
1. Bowl, rose, pink herringbone w/pinched top, camphor ft. 150
2. Bowl, bride's, herringbone, lemon colored, impf. 160
3. Creamer, lemon, square mouth, shiny. 130
4. Creamer, pink, diamond quilted, heart shaped. 165
5. Cruet, pink, herringbone. 190
6. Ewer, raindrop design, shaded rose, camphor handle, 9". 180
7. Cup, punch, pink, herringbone 65
8. Cup, punch, blue raindrop. 60
9. Dish, master, salt, blue D.Q., berry pontil, silver holder. 120
10. Jar, mustard, diamond quilted, blue. 130
11. Lamp Shades, four, D.Q. yellow amber hanging chandelier 48
12. Lamp Shade, 5"D, D.Q., blue, white lining. 40
13. Lamp, table, shade & base rose, D.Q., 12"H. 300
14. Lamp, fairy, tricorn base, rare Tartan patt. Revi p115 1200
15. Mug, pink, D.Q., floral decoration. 110
16. Pitcher, water, blue w/sq. top & reed handle. 350
17. Toothpick, pink herringbone, in silver holder. 195
18. Toothpick, blue satin, D.Q., overlay. 85
19. Toothpick, satin, rose. 60
20. Tumbler, pink herringbone. 60
21. Tumbler, pink diamond quilted. 90
22. Tumbler, butterscotch herringbone. 85
23. Tumbler, blue diamond quilted. 70
24. Tumbler, yellow herringbone. 75
25. Tumbler, square mouth, lemon satin. 80
26. Tumbler, decorated, apricot diamond quilted. 65
27. Tumbler, apricot raindrop. 115
28. Tumbler, water, pink diamond quilted, floral decoration. 125
29. Tumbler, pink diamond quilted, daisy decoration. 150
30. Tumbler, water, blue diamond quilted, floral decoration. 175
31. Tumbler, water, blue diamond quilted, floral decoration. 150
32. Tumbler, decorated, apricot diamond quilted. 105
33. Tumbler, pink raindrop, elaborate decor., rare. 265
34. Vase, 6", green, ruffled top, melon shaped, D.Q. 135
35. Vase, ribbon, miniature, chartreuse top, raindrop. 195

Mother of Pearl - other examples cont'd

36.	Vase, miniature, 3", salmon, diamond quilted.	95
37.	Vase, lemon diamond quilted, w/camphor rim.	115
38.	Vase, miniature w/applied camphor rim, pink D.Q.	125
39.	Vase, pink diamond quilted, miniature.	135
40.	Vase, ruffled top, miniature, blue herringbone.	100
41.	Vase, miniature, ruffled top, diamond quilted.	120
42.	Vase, ruffled fan top, ribbon stripe, miniature, blue.	155
43.	Vase, 5", pink diamond quilted, tricorn, w/ruffled top.	150
44.	Vase, 5", blue D.Q., ruffled top, delicate decoration.	115
45.	Vase, rare 8", chartreuse, dimple sided design.	400
46.	Vase, 5½", ovoid D.Q., decor., rare, white camphor feet.	450

MT. WASHINGTON GLASS

1200

A general term for the several types of glass turned out by the Mount Washington Glass Company of New Bedford, Massachusetts. The history of this company since it was founded in the 19th Century included many famous glassmakers such as Deming Jarves, Frederick Shirley, and the Libbeys. They moved to New Bedford around 1850, but their most famous product, Burmese, was not invented by Shirley until 1885. In addition to this well-known product, others that received wide recognition were Crown Milano, Peach Blow, and Royal Flemish. Some of the lesser known products were Napoli, Verona, and Lava glass. For complete details and examples with prices, refer to the specific type of glass named here.

Picture No. 20 on the Rear Cover is a fine example of their peachblow.

An excellent account of the later work of the Nash family with many fine illustrations of scarce and rare examples of their work is included in Revi's *American Art Nouveau Glass*, pages 94 to 119.

1.	Bowl, rose, 6"D, satin w/enamel decor.	65
2.	Jar, cookie, decor., satin, SP top and handle, 6"H.	180
3.	Shaker, sugar, ribbed satin glass, silver top.	75
4.	Shaker, salt & pepper, round, satin ribbed. pr.	45
5.	Shaker, salt, egg shaped, satin ribbed.	25
6.	Shaker, salt, egg shaped, satin w/enamel decor.	35
7.	Toothpick, spur top, enamel floral decor.	85

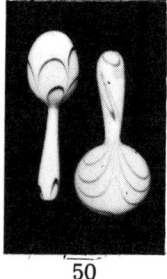

NAILSEA GLASS

50

Named after a factory in Nailsea, England which is credited with first producing this type of glass in modern times. It is characterized by loopings or swags of one color of glass superimposed on a background glass of different color. Flasks and bowls were produced in this decoration probably a little before 1800. This form of decoration was picked up and used by the early American glasshouses before the Art Noveau Period, so technically this style does not fall within the scope of

Nailsea

this book. However, like so many other styles in glassware, they were revived again and again. Steuben made many beautiful stocking darners in the Nailsea form of decoration after 1900. And as usual, European glassmakers are still making some forms at present. Illustration No. 16 on the Front Cover shows the Nailsea type decoration in color.

1. Ball, Witch, 5", clear crystal, white loops. 40
2. Bell, white loops on cranberry, 7"H. 80
3. Bottle, gemel, 6", white background, red loops 100
4. Bowl, 8" square, red and white decoration. 55
5. Bowl, 7" D, crystal with green loops, c1825. 160
6. Darner, stocking, 6", blue and white (Steuben ?) 75
7. Lamp, Fairy, 5½", signed Clarke, blue and white. 140
8. Lamp, Fairy, 5½", three-part rose with white loops. 125
9. Vase, 4", blue background with white loops. 50
10. Bell, cranberry glass w/white swag decor., 14". 100

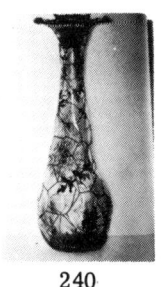

NAPOLI GLASS

A product of the Mt. Washington Glass Company that is not too well known. A signed example is shown in the Grovers' book and is listed below.

Grover Plate Numbers

1. Vase, 10", clear with enamel decoration, signed Napoli. G#107 ....$240
2. Pitcher, 10", clear with crab decoration, not signed. G#108 275

240

NAKARA GLASS

A registered trade marked item of the C. F. Monroe Company of Meriden, Connecticut. This firm (which see) bought opal glass blanks from various glass works and decorated them with different colored enamels. Most of the work was done on blanks designed for utilitarian purposes, such as powder jars, hair receivers, and other boudoir accessories. The decoration was usually of high quality. Almost identical items were produced by this same firm under the names Kelva and Wavecrest (refer to these listings for more examples). Many of the pieces are found marked with these names or the initials C.F.M. See picture under Kelva classification for typical shape and decoration.

120

Grover Plate Numbers
111 Box, powder, 5½", beige w/sailboat decoration. 175

Other Examples
1. Box, dresser, 5", green w/sailing decoration. 75
2. Jar, powder, 4", signed Nakara, good decoration. 45
3. Jardiniere, 12", white w/good decoration, signed. 100
4. Receiver, hair, 3", decorated and signed. 50

47

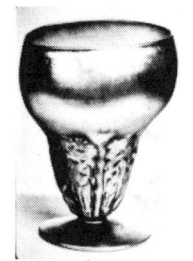

NASH GLASS

Glass produced by Arthur J. Nash and his two sons after the time they were associated with Tiffany. Some of this glass was signed and some was not. Unsigned pieces are almost indistinguishable from Tiffany, as might be expected since these three were deeply involved in the design, manufacture, and distribution of Tiffany's product for a number of years. They went into business for themselves after Louis Tiffany withdrew his name and support around the time of World War I. Prior to his association with Tiffany, Arthur Nash was a skilled glass craftsman in England.

200

Grover Plate Numbers
255 Vase, 5½", stretched gold iridescent. 200
256 Vase, 7½", gold iridescent pull-up decoration, sgn'd. 375

Other Examples
1. Bowl, irides. green, ruffled edge, signed, 10-1/4" 325
2. Bowl, blue w/shaped ruffled rim, enamel decor., sgn'd Wp19 325
3. Box, flue stripped "Chintz", 5"D, w/cover. 185
4. Candlesticks, 12"H, smoke colored, signed. pr. 150
5. Goblet, banded crystal w/rose top. 60
6. Goblet, matted animal stem, bowl crystal (Nash ?) 25
7. Pitcher, amethyst, w/amber handle and foot. 125
8. Vase, gold irides., footed w/fine embossed design. 175

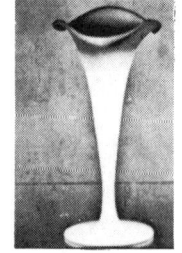

NEW ENGLAND GLASS

When this term is used in connection with Art Glass it is usually in reference to products of the New England Glass Company of Cambridge Mass. which had a long and distinguished history during the better part of the 19th Century when it finally became the Libbey Glass Company and moved to Ohio. Some of the well known Art Glass items were Agata, Amberina, Plated Amberina, Peachblow, and Pomona, which see. Most of these were due to ingenuity of a great glassmaker, Joseph Locke.

400

For a detailed knowledge of all New England glass and the New England Glass Company in particular the new book *New England Glass ard Glassmaking* by Kenneth Wilson, Curator of Glass at the Corning Museum is recommended.

ONYX GLASS

A molded opal-like glass made in Findlay, Ohio, by the firm of Dalzell, Glimore, Leighton Company and therefore sometimes referred to as Findlay Glass. This glass was produced by a patented process which gave it a surface sheen, and the molded daisy-like design has a silvery finish on white or cream colored ware. Other types were made with a colored background such as raspberry color. In this case the characteristic design was in white making a very effective contrast.

650

This was first made in the last decade of the Nineteenth Century and are now sought-after collectors' pieces, even though they were molded and originally made for table use rather than for decorative purposes. See #8 on Front Cover for color picture.

Grover Plate Numbers
410 Syrup, 7", white and gold decoration.	275
411 Spooner, 4", raspberry and white flowers.	800
412 Pitcher, water, 8"H, white w/silver decoration.	650

Other Examples
1. Bowl, sugar, cinnamon.	385
2. Bowl, $2\frac{1}{2}$"D, raspberry and white flowers	1000
3. Bowl, sugar, $3\frac{1}{2}$", cinnamon color & white decoration.	400
4. Creamer, orange	410
5. Creamer, cinnamon.	360
6. Holder, celery, rare butterscotch onyx, $6\frac{1}{2}$" W-p4	600
7. Jar, syrup, with pewter top, white, $7\frac{1}{2}$".	250
8. Jug, syrup, white, with top.	285
9. Muffineer, white, 5".	255
10. Pitcher, cream, $4\frac{1}{2}$", cream color & silver decoration.	250
11. Shaker, sugar, light cinnamon color. 5"	350
12. Shaker, sugar, white, $5\frac{1}{2}$". W-p4	250
13. Spooner, 5", cream with silver decoration.	200
14. Toothpick,	160
15. Toothpick, cinnamon.	295
16. Toothpick, raspberry.	600
17. Tumbler, $3\frac{1}{2}$"H, white w/silver flowers.	205
18. Tumbler, water, 4", raspberry and white flowers.	800
19. Vase, small, silver onyx, fluted neck.	150
20. Vase, 5", cinnamon color and white decoration.	425

OVERLAY GLASS

A broad classification which refers generally to glass produced toward the end of the Victorian period when the very ornate and gaudy designs and decorations were at their height. Even though this glass was made by many glasshouses both here and Europe, there are certain similarities that predominate throughout. Many of the pieces were of cased or lined glass. The inside was white and the shiny outside was plain colored or shaded. Many pieces were footed with camphor or amber glass. Some persons feel that they can tell the source by the shape and design of the feet. The name for this type, however, comes from the applied glass decoration which was "overlaid" on the outside of the piece. Most common among the overlay decoration was thick strands of twisted glass in a contrast to the body color and to which were fastened either flowers or fruits. It is an exception to find such a piece of overlay glass signed. Some people refer to these ornate pieces as Sandwich overlay.

200

Overlay

Grover Plate Numbers
122 Vase, 7", signed Stevens & Williams, amber.	325
123 Vase, 9½", shaded rose, pine cone overlay.	200
124 Vase, 11", strawberry overlay. Illus.	200
125 Bowl, 5½", trumpet flower overlay, footed.	375
126 Vase, 17", rose shaded, overlay fruit, footed.	240
127 Vase, 13", shaded green, cherry overlay.	225

Other Examples
1. Baskets, bride, pr. pink & white on silv. pl. stand, 13½" pr.	300
2. Basket, 9", shaded blue, red & yellow flowers overlaid.	175
3. Basket, 12", shaded red, amber feet, amber decor.	160
4. Bowl, body, white w/leafs & legs in green.	75
5. Bowl, 12", centerpiece, rose & white, elaborate overlay	300
6. Bowls, blue satin w/applied flowers. pr.	100
7. Vase, milk white ground, White House decor., ruffled top	125
8. Vase, 10", rose inside, white outside w/amber overlay.	110
9. Vase, 11", Wheeling type w/pink flowers applied decor.	120
10. Vase, 12", red over white, applied leaves and flowers.	90
11. Vase, 12", white with amber decoration and fruits.	250
12. Vase, 8", cased blue over white, applied clear decor.	60

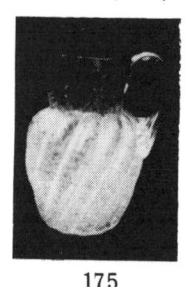

OVERSHOT GLASS

This glass has a rough surface purposely applied to simulate a heavily frosted or iced glass. This was produced and known under several other names. It was produced over many, many years by a number of techniques which resulted in different surface finishes. The type commonly referred to as Overshot has a sandblasted surface. There is a great tendency for any of this type of glass to be attributed to the Boston & Sandwich Glass Company and therefore called "Sandwich" overshot.

175

1. Basket, brides, 9", reeded handle, overshot crystal finish	120
2. Bowl, 8", cranberry color in overshot finish	175
3. Pitcher, 9", water, overshot finish	140
4. Pitcher, 5", cream, cranberry overshot finish	125
5. Toothpick, 2", heavy crackle finish in blue	50
6. Tumbler, water, clear overshot finish.	30
7. Vase, 8", tankard shape in overshot finish, crystal.	50

PAIRPOINT GLASS

Any product of the Pairpoint Manufacturing Company which absorbed the Mt. Washington Glass Company of New Bedford, Massachusetts, in the latter part of the Nineteenth Century. The term "Pairpoint" today is applied to a very limited type of glass attributed to this company. These are colored crystal pieces having a clear crystal ball in the stems of all footed pieces. The crystal ball has a series of small bubbles in a regular pattern. The blue is usually a cobalt. Other colors

80

Pairpoint

are green, cranberry, and amber. Sometimes this product is confused with a similar colored crystal of Steuben because of the similarity in shapes. They are reported to have made paperweights. A crystal one with spiral bubbles is typical.

A fine book on glass made by the Pairpoint Company is now out of print. The name is the *Pairpoint Story* by Avila.

1. Compote, 8", cranberry, bubble ball stem   pr.   160
2. Compote, 8", green, crystall ball stem. Illus.   70
3. Compote, pr. 7", red intaglio cut, crystal ball stem   pr.   200
4. Goblet, 6", cranberry, footed with crystal ball   25
5. Lamp, on bronze stand, pumpkin shape, 16". W-p29   300
6. Vase, 8", green intaglio cut, crystal ball stem.   75
7. Vase, 10", trumpet shape, cobalt crystal ball stem.   60
8. Vase, cameo glass w/grape motif, 14½", sgn'd. W-p25   575

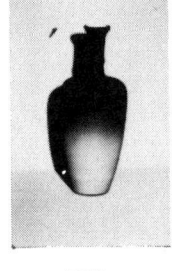

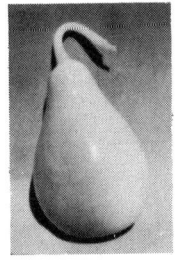

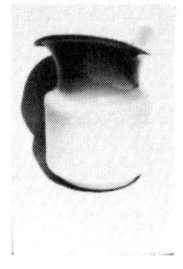

700   125   400   250

PEACHBLOW GLASS

A term borrowed from very old Chinese porcelain and applied to reproductions of this ware about 1885. Generally, the several different types can be defined as dual color shaded opaque glass articles. The shading in all cases was produced by using a heat-sensitive glass which, after forming, was returned to the furnace where a portion of it was reheated. The second heating turned the hottest portion a darker color (usually red obtained from a gold compound). The gradation of color follows the temperature range so that the unheated portion remained unchanged in color.

The three principal types of Peachblow are Wheeling Peachblow made by Hobbs, Brockunier & Company of Wheeling, West Virginia; New England Peachblow, produced at the same time by the New England Glass Company; and Mt. Washington Peachblow, made by the Mt. Washington Glass Company of New Bedford, Massachusetts. Several other types which were very similar were made in England, and the Rockwell Gallery in Corning has a piece made by Mr. Carder of the Steuben Glass Company. There are other shaded pieces of glass that are sometimes incorrectly called peachblow which is confusing to the beginner. Only authentic examples of the above three warrant the high prices of this sought-after type of glass. Details on the colors and construction are given below for each of the three types together with examples and prices. Also refer to Gunderson, Sandwich, Stevens & Williams, and Webb that also produced glass called Peachblow.

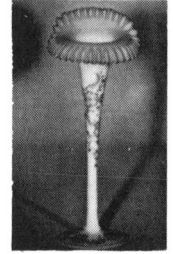

PEACHBLOW — MT. WASHINGTON

4250

Mt. Washington Peachblow was produced at the works at New Bedford, Massachusetts, about 1886 in competition with the other makes. This is a single layer of opaque heat-sensitive glass when properly treated, shades from a grayish rose color at the top to a grayish blue at the bottom. All examples listed below are in the dull acid finish. It commands a premium price for fine colored specimens, as pieces are very scarce and the demand high. The same color shading goes completely through the single layer of glass. See color picture, top left, on Rear Cover.

Grover Plate Numbers
72. Pitcher, 7", decorated with verse and daisies.	4500
73. Bowl, 2", acid finish, daisy decorated, fine color.	2100
74a Bowl, sugar, $3\frac{1}{2}$", crimped top, fair acid color.	1600
74b Pitcher, creamer, $5\frac{1}{2}$", crimped top, fair color.	2400
75. Vase, 7", footed, rare deep color.	1800
76. Vase, 8", stick acid finish, decorated, good color.	3200
77. Vase, $10\frac{1}{2}$", jack, crimped edge, decor., light color.	4200

Other Examples
1. Bowl, 4", finger, pinched edge, excellent color.	1800
2. Bowl, 4", low scalloped top, unusual diamond quilted.	1500
3. Creamer, footed, imperfect.	450
4. Toothpick, exquisite daisy decoration.	1600
5. Tumbler, enamel decoration, 3-1/4"H.	1600
6. Tumbler, water, 4", rare daisy decoration, acid finish	1750
7. Pitcher, cream, 5", rare hobnail, good color, minor rep.	1750
8. Vase, classic shape, fair color, 9".	600
9. Vase, lily, ruffled edge, h.p. daisy decor. $10\frac{1}{2}$", W-p32	4000
10. Vase, 9", bottle shaped, fair coloring.	1000

PEACHBLOW — NEW ENGLAND

750

The New England Peachblow was originally called Wild Rose and shades from a heavy rose at the top to a white at the bottom. Since it is made of a single layer of glass, the shading is identical inside and out. Both glossy and dull finish examples are found. The richer coloring usually brings a premium price. Usually pieces were not signed.

Grover Plate Numbers
67. Vase, 11", bulbous, dull finish.	500
68. Bowl, $2\frac{1}{2}$", finger, acid, crimped edge.	400
69. Pitcher, $6\frac{1}{2}$", excellent shiny color.	750
70. Vase, 18", trumpet, fine shiny color.	500
71. Vase, 8", stick, pair, one shiny, one dull. pr.	800

Peachblow - New England   Other Examples

1. Bowl, rose, 5"D, fine color, decorated, acid finish. — 300
2. Creamer, square mouth, dull finish, excellent color. — 350
3. Cup, punch, 2", excellent color, dull acid finish — 250
4. Darner, stocking, good color, shiny. — 65
5. Figure, shape of pear, good color & stem. W-p33 — 125
6. Figure, pear, open end stem. — 100
7. Figure, pear, good color. — 100
8. Holder, toothpick, tricorn. — 190
9. Holder, toothpick, 2-1/4"H, sq. mouth. — 220
10. Pitcher, creamer, 4", good dull color. — 275
11. Set, creamer & sugar, "World's Fair 1893". — 500
12. Shade, 9"D, acid finish, fair color, brass hanging lamp. — 185
13. Spooner, 5", ruffle top, good color, shiny — 225
14. Shade, lamp, 14", with lamp, hobnail, fine color. — 400
15. Tumbler, 3½"H, shiny, good color. — 205
16. Tumbler, acid finish, good color. 3"H. — 180
17. Tumbler, whiskey, acid finish, weak color, 2"H. — 145
18. Tumbler, water, acid finish. — 215
19. Tumbler, water, shiny finish, very good color. — 225
20. Tumbler, whiskey, 2½", excellent color, acid finish. — 275
21. Tumbler, water, 4", good color, shiny. — 200
22. Vase, with crimped edge. 4-1/4". — 250

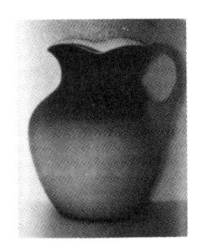

PEACHBLOW — WHEELING

875

This third major type of Peachblow was produced at the Hobbs, Brockunier Company in Wheeling, West Virginia. This is the only one of the three that is a two-layered glass. The inside lining is white and the outside layer is shaded from rich deep red to a soft attractive yellow by the final heat treatment. Color in this ware varies from light to dark and from garish to rich raspberry and yellow. Both acid and shiny examples were made, each one being sought after in fine coloring. One well-known shape in this is the so-called Morgan Vase, named after the original owner of the Chinese porcelain vase that inspired the production of all of the Peachblows. (See lower right illustration on Front Cover.) The base on these vases is a separate molded amber glass stand, having five Griffins for legs. These were made shiny and dull to match the accompanying vase. These in mint condition are harder to find than the Morgan vase and therefore command a disproportionate price as shown below.

Grover Plate Numbers

78. Pitcher, 5", clear handle, shiny, drape pattern fair color — 650
79. Pitcher, water, 7", excellent acid coloring. — 875
80. Set, creamer & sugar, in silver holder, shiny. — 1400
81. Decanter, 9", acid fine color, amber handle and stopper — 850
82. Pitcher, 10", exceptional color, amber ring handle. — 775
83a Vase, 10", Morgan style and stand, good, shiny. — 900

Peachblow - Wheeling - cont'd.
83b Vase, 10", Morgan style and stand, fine color, dull. 1000
84. Jug, syrup, 7", pewter top, shiny, fine color. 625
85. Cruet, 7", vinegar, acid finish, good color. 675
86. Tumbler, water, 4", acid finish, good color. 250
87. Vase, 8", stick, fine shaded color, acid finish. 550

Other Examples
1. Base, 2", of Morgan style vase, acid finish, mint. 350
2. Bottle, claret, dull finish, good color. 500
3. Bottle, water, 7", pyramid shape, fine color, shiny. 600
4. Cruet, vinegar, 5", acid finish, excellent color. 750
5. Cruet, bulbous, shiny finish. 600
6. Cruet, petticoat, acid, very good color. 625
7. Cup, punch, 2", good color, amber handle, shiny. 225
8. Cup, punch, acid finish, w/handle. 200
9. Ewers, 8", pair, shiny with rigaree decoration.   pr. 2000
10. Pitcher, water, $8\frac{1}{2}$"H, acid finish, fair color. 625
11. Pitcher, creamer, $4\frac{1}{2}$", square mouth, deep color, dull fin. 650
12. Pitcher, water, 8", tricorn top, amber handle, fine color. 800
13. Set, salt & pepper. 225
14. Set, condiment, 2 cruets & muffineer, silver holder, scarce 1800
15. Set, lemonade, covered tankard pitcher, 6 tumblers. 1750
16. Shaker, sugar, 5", silver top, good color, dull acid finish. 275
17. Tumbler, water, shiny, fair color. 200
18. Tumbler, water, 5", good color. 170
19. Tumbler, water, shiny, good color. 235
20. Tumbler, water, dull finish. 245
21. Tumbler, $3\frac{1}{2}$"H, acid, fine color. 270
22. Vase, bud, slender 9", yellow to red. 350
23. Vase, w/plastic holder. 700
24. Vase, miniature 2-1/4", acid finish, gold decoration. 550
25. Vase, gourd shape, gold enamel decoration, butterfly. 500
26. Vase, 8", Morgan shape, shiny finish, no base, fair color. 600
27. Vase, 8", Morgan shape, acid finish weak coloring. 500
28. Vase, Morgan shape, glossy, amber base, 10". 1000
29. Vase, Morgan shape, w/acid finish, no base. 7-3/4". 700
30. Vase, celery, 6", narrow waist, satisfactory acid color. 290

PEACHBLOW — Other Types

In addition to the well-documented and defined types of Peachblow there are many variations of this shaded heat sensitive glass that to date have not been definitely attributed to a particular glasshouse. For example, in the Rockwell collection there is a piece of Peachblow that was made by Mr. Carder while at Steuben. Sandwich Peachblow is supposed to have apricot-peach to white appearance although Wilson in his latest book on *New England Glass & Glassmakers* does not mention this.

Because of this lack of authentication and definite known characteristics, the odd types of Peachblow-like items usually sell for a small fraction of what the well defined ones do even though many of these "odd" ones are equally attractive in color and design.

Peachblow - Other Types

Grover Plate Numbers

88. Bowl, punch, 10½", glossy finish, fine color.   600
89. Basket, Sandwich type, 10½", swirl, camphor handle.   500

Other Examples
1. Bottle, cologne, Webb type, lined, fine color, 5"H.   275
2. Bowl, Sandwich type, 8"D, ruffled top.   350
3. Bowl, rose, Sandwich (?), peach to white.   60
4. Vase, 8", Webb type, lined, good color.   300
5. Vase, N.Martinsville, 9"H, pink to cream.   175

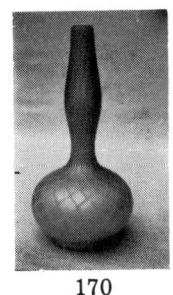

PEARL SATINGLASS (Pearl Glass)

A term used in Victorian times for the glass that is commonly referred to today as Mother of Pearl Satin Glass. (See Section under this heading for more details.) This is essentially double-layered glass which has air trapped between the two opaque layers in regular or irregular patterns, such as Diamond Quilted, Raindrop, and many others. The effect of the air between the two surfaces imparted an opalescent or pearly illusion in those areas and contrasted with the opaque color of the outer layer to give a very pleasing appearance. Mr. Revi in his book *Nineteenth Century Glass* has a very complete story under this title.

170

PEKING GLASS

This term as currently used refers to opaque glass articles presumably of Chinese origin which simulate in shapes, colors, and finishes much older antique ware. To date there has not been anything definitive published but pieces by this name have appeared infrequently at sales and auctions of Art Glass. The best pictorial record of this ware is in Whitlow's *Art Colored and Cameo Glass* which is now out of print. About a dozen pieces are shown in typical Chinese shapes and colors on page 46. Since many of these resemble cameo glass caution should be exercised in assuming they were all produced by this most costly method. Usually this glass is offered at modest prices and should not be assumed to be old unless it is thoroughly documented.

130

1. Bottle, snuff, 2-1/4", green design on white.   40
2. Urn, Chinese glass, covered min., w/fitted teakwood stand.   75
3. Vase, 12"H, bulbous, w/long neck, oxblood scene on white.   120
4. Vase, 8"H, Ming yellow relief floral design on same base.   60

PELOTON GLASS

A fine decorative type of glass that is characterized by what appear to be various different colored streaks in short random lengths and shapes in the surface of the article which is often an opal white. Mr. Revi traces its origin to a patent by Kralick about 1880 in what is now Czechoslovakia. The effect is produced by working short pieces of thin glass threads of many different colors into the body of glass while it is still in the plastic state, so that it is flush and appears to be a part of the original gather. This is similar to the random threading wound on the surface of some Steuben pieces and then marvered (rolled) into the surface while the glass is hot. The main difference between the two is that Peloton used short lengths while Steuben rolled continuous threads. Whether many factories made this product is not known.

Grover Nos.
386 Jar, biscuit, 7", silver top and handle. 300
387 Plate, 7", one color on transparent. 160
388 Vase, 9", colored pieces on white. 250

Other Examples
1. Jar, 6"D, with cover, milk glass & colored pieces. 185
2. Vase, miniature, 3"H, violet, applied glass legs. 150
3. Vase, 8"H, shredded cocoanut flaired blown glass. 240
4. Vases, pair, 13", Peloton type decorations. pr. 380

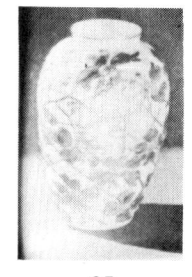

PHOENIX

A product of the Phoenix Glass Company which made a wide variety of different kinds in Beaver County, Pennsylvania. The pieces currently referred to by this name are molded with various designs in high relief in the manner of cameo or sculptured glass. This effect is obtained by covering the high portions with a color that contrasts with the base. Most of this production was probably made during the 1930's and was very modestly priced.

While this is not what is generally classed as Art Glass it is covered here because of its similarity and the current interest as evidenced at recent auction sales. A typical piece is shown on the rear cover, Illustration No. 23.

1. Bowl, 10"D, sculptured glass in white & glove gray. 35
2. Compote, amethyst pastel w/ped. base, dolphin design, 6". 100
3. Shades, gas, set of four, signed. set 70
4. Vase, flower, $9\frac{1}{2}$", apricot two-toned. 45
5. Vase, white relief decor. of dancing females. 12" 75
6. Vase, table, 10", baluster shape, red on white floral. 50
7. Vase, art glass in apricot color, 7". 50
8. Vase, sculptured, in green and white, $10\frac{1}{2}$". 70
9. Vase, 11", embossed brown & green floral design. 75

PINK SLAG GLASS

650

This term is usually applied to one pattern of this opaque pressed glass made by the Indiana Tumbler and Goblet Company in Greentown, Indiana, who made a number of different wares and patterns. See Custard Glass for more details. The pattern is known as Inverted Fan and Feather and is another example of items included in the Art Glass category because of a coupling of limited production with a high demand by collectors. Most of the known pieces were of the tableware variety and not made for decorative purposes as were some of the fine types of glass. The pink color varies in tone and density but with no clear lines of demarcation as in Purple Slag, or the marbled, or stoneware types. The deeper colors command a premium; the small cabinet size also are disproportionally high in price.

Grover Plate Numbers
413 Cruet, vinegar, $6\frac{1}{2}$", IF & F pattern, extremely fine colors. 650
414 Pitcher, water, 8", IF & F pattern, good coloring. 550
415 Sugar, $5\frac{1}{2}$", covered IF & F pattern, light colors. 250
416 Pitcher, cream, $4\frac{1}{2}$", IF & F pattern, light colors. 240

Other Examples
1. Bowl, sugar, weak color. 200
2. Compote, jelly, 5", IF & F pattern, light coloring. 350
3. Cruet, satisfactory color, repaired. 90
4. Cup, punch, fair color. 155
5. Dish, butter, covered, IF & F pattern, fine coloring. 650
6. Dish, sauce, footed, weak color. 60
7. Dish, butter w/dome cover, rare, footed, $7\frac{1}{2}$". 325
8. Dish, sauce, footed, good color. 165
9. Holder, toothpick, fair coloring. 200
10. Holder, toothpick, good coloring. 250
11. Holder, toothpick, finest rich coloring. 360
12. Pitcher, cream, good color. 250
13. Tumbler, $3\frac{1}{2}$"H, water. 250
14. Tumbler, water, very good coloring. 275
15. Tumbler, grape & vine design. 35

PLATED AMBERINA GLASS

1200

Plated Amberina forms the apex of the pyramid of the many heat-sensitive shaded glasswares made in the last years of the Nineteenth Century. Descriptively named as a combination of Amberina glass and a casing or "plating" of a different color. The different color is the opalescent white lining over which the casing or plating of heat-sensitive amber glass laid. A differential in temperature was created by only introducing part of it into the glory hole of the furnace. The hottest portion, usually the top, turned to the characteristic deep fuschia red because

Plated Amberina

of the gold in the compound. The cooler portions remained the original amber color. One other essential feature of the type of glass is the vertical ribbing which gives additional distinction to this very scarce and sought-after collector's dream. A patented ware of the New England Glass Company, it differs from the lined or plated Wheeling Peachblow in that the lining is opalescent and the pieces are ribbed. Not found signed.

Grover Plate Numbers
11. Pitcher, water, 7", good coloring.   3400
12. Pitcher, cream, fine coloring. Revi p. 30   2700
13. Pitcher, syrup, 6", silver top, very fine coloring.   2800
14. Tumbler, lemonade, 5", excellent colors.   1200
15. Bowl, finger, 3", fluted edge, good color.   1500
16. Bowl, 3", scalloped edge, finest coloring.   2200

Other Examples
1. Bowl, large, 8", beautiful example & color.   3000
2. Bowl, 8", scalloped edge, good coloring.   2500
3. Pitcher, cream, 5", excellent color and ribs.   2750
4. Shaker, salt & pepper, good coloring.   2500
5. Spooner, 5", light colors.   1100
6. Toothpick, 2"H, outstanding color & ribs.   1325
7. Tumbler, lemonade, low handle, 5"H, average color.   950
8. Tumbler, water, good coloring.   950
9. Tumbler, lemonade, 8", low handle, fine coloring.   1200
10. Tumbler, water, 4", good colors and ribbing.   1000
11. Vase, bud, lily, metal stand, fair color, $10\frac{1}{2}$".   1850
12. Vase, 8", lily shaped, average coloring.   1200

POMONA GLASS

A transparent crystal glass with a design produced in relief by acid etching. The process is similar to that done on heavier pieces and referred to as Acid cutback. In the finest pieces the design and top edge have been further stained, usually in yellows or blues and fired to set the stain. This throws the clear crystal design left by the etching in sharper contrast with the matte finished acid surface that surrounds the design. The overall effect is one of lightness and daintiness. This was one more of the patented developments by the famous glassworker Joseph Locke and assigned to the New England Glass Company. Like any glass that has been decorated by a fired stain, the surface color will deteriorate with wear and abrasion. The finer the design and condition the more desirable the piece. Original production was made by scribing fine lines in the acid resist for the background. This is known as First Grind. Later to save expense a cheaper method was devised. This is called Second Grind.

175

Grover Plate Numbers
99. Pitcher, water, 12", tankard, first grind, butterfly.   800
100 Goblet, water, 6", second grind, blue cornflower.   200
101 Vase, spoon, 5", second grind, blueberry decor. Illus.   175

Pomona - other examples, cont'd

1.	Bowl, sugar, 4", blueberry	160
2.	Bowl, ruffled finger, second grind, earthworm decor.	90
3.	Cruet, 6", first grind, clear handle and stopper.	225
4.	Cup, punch, second grind, blackberry.	80
5.	Cup, punch, $2\frac{1}{2}$", inverted acanthus leaves.	120
6.	Cup, punch, cornflower decoration.	65
7.	Dish, butter w/dome cover, first grind, 8".	250
8.	Goblet, water, 6", stemmed, no design, first grind.	110
9.	Holder, toothpick, tricorn, D.Q., first grind.	80
10.	Holder, toothpick, 2"H, rigaree decor., first grind.	85
11.	Holder, toothpick, 2"H, scalloped.	55
12.	Pitcher, 4", first grind, blueberry design.	280
13.	Pitcher, tankard, w/six tumblers, D.Q., impf.	275
14.	Tumbler, water, 4", butterfly and pansy decoration.	115
15.	Tumbler, water, 4", second grind, cornflower design.	95
16.	Tumbler, water, diamond quilted, scalloped.	60
17.	Tumbler, water, second grind, pansy & butterfly decor.	90
18.	Tumbler, water, cornflower design.	105
19.	Tumbler, water, first grind, good color & design, $3\frac{1}{2}$".	120
20.	Vase, fan shaped, footed, first grind.	300

PATTERN-PRESSED GLASS

85

This classification of glass is included here not as a type of Art Glass but to group together several varieties shown elsewhere under other named classifications. For example, under the classification of Amberina Items 9 and 21 are examples of this type of glass that were made by pressing in the famous Daisy & Button Pattern. There is so much of this pattern on the market in clear and single colors as well as many reproductions that it is one of the most common patterns to be found. Therefore, the only reason that this inexpensive and common type item is listed under Art Glass is that a very small percentage of the output was made by combining this very ordinary method with one of the very desirable formulations of shaded, heat-sensitive glass. Other examples of pressed glass in this book are products of the C. F. Monroe Company, Holly Amber, Star Holly & Klondike. In all cases, ware produced by very ordinary means was made desirable and appealing by further treatment and decorative methods.

QUEZEL GLASS

600

The name Quezel is associated with that period of glass history when the popularity of iridescent glass was at its height both here and in Europe. About 1900 when the Quezel Art Glass and Decorating Company was founded, Tiffany and Steuben were producing the same types of glass. The fact that Martin Bach, the founder of the company, previously worked for Tiffany resulted in items that are difficult to distinguish from the products of this latter company. While Quezel

Quezel Continued

products were not limited to iridescent wares, the scope of their output did not approach either Steuben or Tiffany in ingenuity or variety. Much of the Quezel iridescent glass is decorated with designs made by various techniques of adding threaded glass, such as feather type designs formed by hooking the threads to formed looped effects and then rolling them down into the body of the glass. Some of the product was signed "Quezel" in slanted block letters.

Grover Plate Numbers

229 Vase, 10", gold irides. w/silver overlay, signed.	500
230 Vase, 6", reddish gold irides., lightning design, sgn'd.	550
231 Vase, 11", gold irides. & green tipped feathers, sgn'd.	750
232 Vase, 5", decorated dark blue irides., signed.	800
233 Vase, 8", gold & white, gold tipped green feathers, sgn'd.	600
234 Vase, 12", gold & white, feathers and lily pads, signed.	700

Other Examples

1. Bowl, miniature, ribbed gold irides., signed.	200
2. Bowl, irides. gold with fluted edge, 7".	250
3. Bowl, rare, 12", shallow, golden irides., signed.	250
4. Compote, gold irides., pedestal base, 6", signed.	200
5. Compote, 7", gold irides., signed.	240
6. Lamp, 14", hanging, w/four small ones on arms.	700
7. Lamp, hanging, 10"D, pearl green & gold decor.	250
8. Lamp, shades, set of four, pearl w/gold feather design.	165
9. Plate, saucer, stretch glass, signed, 7".	170
10. Shade, lamp, gold tropical leaf design.	50
11. Shades, lamp, two iridescent.	43
12. Tazza, gold irides., hand chased, sterling base, 11".W-p3	800
13. Vase, 10", Egyptian design, signed	375
14. Vase, 8"H, gold rainbow irides., signed.	200
15. Vase, leaf & vine on black background, $12\frac{1}{2}$"	450
16. Vase, gold lustre, signed, sterling leaf & flower jacket.	500
17. Vase, footed, black & blue silver swirls & gold interior, 8".	900
18. Vase, Jack-in-Pulpit, irides., peacock feather patt., signed.	350
19. Vase, peg, very fine, sterling silver holder.	240
20. Vase, 8", gold irides., signed.	210
21. Vase, 7", irides. gold w/applied silver decor., signed.	350
22. Wine, 6", gold iridescent, signed.	240

Rainbow Mother of Pearl   Rainbow Satin Glass

650   750   375   400

RAINBOW MOTHER OF PEARL SATIN GLASS

A conventional Mother of Pearl Glass in all respects except the color. Instead of a single uniform or shaded color, this type of glass was multi-colored, with red, blue and yellow in alternating stripes or panels and hence the name "Rainbow." Sometimes the effect is quite pronounced and other times very subdued. In any event it is rare in the Mother Of Pearl Satin Glass category and therefore always commands a premium price. Many examples of this ware are listed under the general heading of Mother Of Pearl Satin Glass, which see. One very unusual form of multi-colored ware is not strictly speaking Rainbow, but is mentioned here as it hardly warrants a separate classification. This is called Tartan Glass. The Fairy Lamp illustrated on page 115 of Revi's book NINETEENTH CENTURY GLASS is an example that is listed below. The criss-cross multi-colored striping was done to simulate the Scotch tartan plaids. A few additional examples of Rainbow are also included below. See illustration #25 on

Grover Plate Numbers
23. Vase, 11"H, alternating blue & pink stripes. 700
31. Pitcher, 7½"H, D.Q., excellent coloring. 750
32. Bowl, rose, D.Q., ribbed, good colors. 650
33. Lamp, shade & font, brass mount., D.Q. 1000
34. Bowl, 7"D, footed, folded & ruffled top, D.Q. 575
35. Ewer, 8½"H, herringbone design, good colors. 600
36. Basket, herringbone design, camphor handle. 750

Other Examples
1. Basket, herringbone, w/camphor handle. 1700
2. Box, 8", on thorn feet, five colors, raindrop pattern. 700
3. Bowl, finger, underplate, rainbow herringbone. 750
4. Ewer, 8", good colors on D.Q., camphor handle. 750
5. Lamp, Fairy, tricorn base, Tartan coloring, Revi.p115 1500
6. Tumbler, water, D.Q., rainbow, enamel floral decor. 625
7. Tumbler, water, 4", five colors on D.Q. 550
8. Vase, 7", diamond quilted, ruffled top. 550
9. Vase, footed, D.Q., 650

RAINBOW SATIN GLASS

As the term implies, this is the use of several colors to produce a rainbow effect on dull, acid finished glass as contrasted with the similar decoration on the Mother of Pearl Satin Glass mentioned before. Somtiemes the multi-colored rainbow design is only applied to a portion of the piece. The rest is in a contrasting white satin finish. See illustration #23 on Rear Cover for a typical piece.

1. Epergne, 14", white satin lilies (4), rainbow inside tops. 375
2. Tumbler, water, 4", alternating stripes of five colors. 150
3. Vase, 8", wide stripes in red, yellow and blue. 200
4. Vase, petite, silver holder. 150

ROSE AMBER GLASS

A term used by the Mt. Washington Glass Company for a product to all intents and purposes the same as Amberina as patented and produced by the New England Glass Company. This name has now been superseded by the general term of Amberina applied to products of any maker in any period of time. For more details on Rose Amber, consult NINETEENTH CENTURY ART GLASS by A. C. Revi.

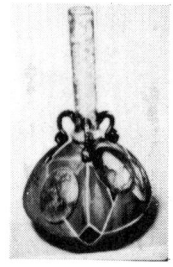

ROYAL FLEMISH GLASS

1200

Visualize a glass article made as a stained glass window is made and you will have a picture that approximates the appearance of this highly individual product of the Mt. Washington Glass Company and marketed by them in the 1890's. Unlike stained glass which is made up of individual pieces of glass separated by thin supporting webs of lead, Royal Flemish is one continuous piece of glass that has been decorated with colored enamels in random panels separated by gold enamel ribs to create the same effect. This glass is frequently characterized by the browns, reds, and tans used for the various sections. Sometimes superimposed on the enamel decoration will be further enamel decoration in the form of old Roman coin or other medals. While some of these pieces are signed, the lack of signature does not detract from this most desirable glass because of the originality of its design and single source of manufacture. Other motifs were used retaining the gold enamel ribs. See illustration on rear cover for picture of outstanding piece.

Grover Plate Number

62. Vase, 15", decorated with ducks.	1750
63. Ewer, 15½", rope handle, basic design overlaid.	1100
64. Pitcher, 9", tan and brown, red scrolls.	1250
65. Vase, 13", panelled design of camel and rider.	3500
66. Jar, cracker, silver top & handle, br. &tan. Revi p77	900

Other Examples

1. Ewer, 16", covered, rope handle, coat of arms decor.	2750
2. Jar, cookie, floral design in tan & brown.	825
3. Jar, biscuit, medallions, silver mount & lid. W-p45	900
4. Lamp, base, 8", in tan and reds, many gold scrolls	950
5. Pitcher, cream, 3", sections in reds and tans.	550
6. Vase, 7½", double-handled, brown & tans, Medallions	850

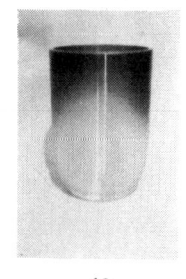

RUBINA GLASS

40

A shaded glass that is ruby or deep cranberry at the top and clear crystal at the bottom. It is thought that this was developed about the time Amberina was so popular in the 1880's. This ware was produced by a number of different companies and apparently in a number of different ways. One method resulted in a gradual shading from ruby to clear while another, like the illustration on the cover, shows an abrupt line of demarcation rather than an even transition. According

Rubina

to Mr. Revi these methods were used to circumvent the patents held by New England Glass Company for the production of Amberina and other shaded wares from heat-sensitive glass.

1. Bowl, 8", good color and shading, fine enamel designs. 100
2. Carafe, water, 8", cranberry to clear, see color Illus. 27 75
3. Candlesticks, 9", pair, deep cranberry to clear. 170
4. Jar, biscuit, silver plated top. W-p22 80
5. Tumbler, water, 4", gradual shading, good color. 20
6. Tumbler, water, 4", deep cranberry to clear, enamel decor. 28
7. Vase, 10", footed, ruby to clear, applied crystal decor. 75
8. Vase, 8", hand painted enamel decoration. 60

RUBINA VERDE GLASS

Similar to Rubina glass except that the shading goes from the same ruby or deep cranberry to a pale greenish yellow at the bottom. This glass was made during the later part of the Nineteenth Century in competition with Amberina. Other color combinations were made in shaded glass, and of course Steuben made a whole series of shaded glass using several colors in vaes and bowls.

1. Basket, brides, in silver holder, 8"D. 120
2. Bowl, and undertray, folded edge. 125
3. Bowl, 7", scalloped, top and fine gold enamel designs. 100
4. Bowl, 5", rose, hobnail design, crimped top. 40
5. Decanter, squat thin neck, enamel design. 150
6. Pitcher, 9", water, thumprint design, typical colors. 120
7. Syrup jug, 5", silver top, inverted thumbprint. 75
8. Tumbler, water, 4", D.Q., good colors. 40
9. Vase, 8", good shading, w/heavy decoration. 90
10. Vase, footed with crimped edge, 6-3/4". 60
11. Vase, enameled cranberry to light green, 10". 80

SANDWICH GLASS

20

25

This loosely applied term refers to the products of the Boston & Sandwich Glass Company of Cape Cod, Massachusetts. As one of the best known and longest lived glass firms, in business for over sixty years, a great quantity of many different kinds and styles of glass was produced there from the time it started in 1826. Blown, molded, pressed, cut, engraved, decorated, cased, overlay, overshot and many other types were produced. Unfortunately the record of this work is very scant. Little of the production was signed. Apparently none of the designs or types were patented. Therefore, there is much supposition as to whether an unmarked piece was made at Sandwich or one of the many competing factories. It is regrettable that through the years people in their anxiety to upgrade some of their acquistions have erroneously attributed them to Sandwich origin. In the period covered by this book some of the Art Glass produced at Sandwich has been documented by family records, such as the

Sandwich Glass (Miscellaneous) - cont'd

Painted Amberina pitcher shown in Grovers' book, ART GLASS NOUVEAU in plate #133. Any items that may have been made at Sandwich are listed separately by the type of glass, such as Fireglow, Cut Velvet, Peachblow miscellaneous, and other like classifications.

1.	Base, lamp font in cranberry w/engraved design.	150
2.	Basket, brides, 9"D, overshot crystal, no holder.	75
3.	Bottle, triple cased with cut windows, 8"H.	250
4.	Bowl, 5"D, heavy lacy pattern in crystal.	50
5.	Candlesticks, pair, dolphin base in blue, cups in white. pr.	175
6.	Dish, salt, master, in shape of boat, lacy.	35
7.	Holder, curtain tie-back in opalescent glass, 4".	35
8.	Lamps, oil, blue milk base & pumpkin font, 12". pr.	220
9.	Pitcher, cream, pressed diamond point.	65
10.	Pitcher, overshot tankard style in green.	125
11.	Plate, cup, in overall lacy design.	20
12.	Plate, clear with relief decoration, octagonal shape.	60
13.	Vase, 10"H, cranberry cut to clear in roundels.	150

SATIN GLASS

Today the glass that was produced during the Victorian period with opaque body and dulled by an acid treatment so that it had a soft uniform matte appearance is given the name Satin Glass. From this very broad grouping many named sub-groups have been developed such as Mother of Pearl, the Peachblows, Fireglow, and Cameo glasses. As with these, some of the Satin Glass products were shaded and some were decorated, threaded or otherwise embellished. This type of glass was produced by many of the houses in America and Europe. Very little of it was signed and, therefore, aside from the well-defined categories, such

500

1	Basket, bride's, rose satin decorated w/thorn handle.	150
2	Bottle, barber, with swirl pattern.	90
3	Bowl, rose, lavender, herringbone pattern.	225
4	Bowl, pink quilted berry.	50
5	Bowls, set of 6 finger, D.Q., $4\frac{1}{2}$". set	100
6	Bowl, rose, D.Q. pattern, chartreuse, gold enamel flowers	350
7	Caster, pickle, lustreless, silver plated mount. Mt. Wash.	110
8	Ewer, ice blue to blue, ruffled edge & rosetree handle.	125
9	Ewers, pair, decorated blue satin, camphor handle. pr.	180
10	Ewer, ice blue, enamel decor., ruffled & overfired edge.	80
11	Jar, biscuit, 7", pink quilted satin, silver top & handle.	70
12	Lamps, pair, oil, swirl, pink to dark rose, metal ped. pr.	500
13	Lamp, miniature, pink satin glass.	125
14	Pitcher, ruffled top, small, blue.	125
15	Pitcher, milk, very rare, blue, diamond quilted.	350
16	Tumbler, water, decorated, pink.	125
17	Tumbler, water, blue, diamond quilted pattern.	50
18	Vase, 18", blue satin w/iris decoration.	125
19	Vase, 8", gourd shape, blue satin.	60
20	Vase, 8", white satin, green lined and ribbed.	60

SCHNEIDER GLASS

A mottled shaded glass of French origin, that is appearing infrequently at some shows and sales. The shapes and colors seem to fall into a relatively narrow range. Most of the pieces are signed with the name Schneider with orange and reds as the predominating colors. Some pieces are shaded and all have a mottled secondary color often darker than the body color.

Grover Plate Number
37. Pitcher, 6½", mottled orange to opal.   120

Other Examples
1. Centerpiece, 14", footed, red with black mottling. W-p25   140
2. Compote, blue on metal stand, 8".   170
3. Compote, marbleized glass, 12".   125
4. Compote, 7", blue mottled in black metal holder. W-p25   170
5. Vase, 10", rose to cream colored in metal holder. W-p25.   125
6. Vase, reddish & amber color, w/metal cage, signed. 11½"   125
7. Vase, 18", gr. glass w/amethyst base.   140

SILVERED GLASS

Glass produced in the Nineteenth Century which was treated on the inside with silver or mercury to give the effect of a silver piece coated with glass. Many fine examples with engravings and cut windows through colored casings were made in Europe. Apparently little of it was made in America and to this day it does not seem to have aroused the enthusiasm of avid collectors, although a good example adds distinction to any collection. Possibly the similarity between this and the thin double-walled Mercury Glass produced in the early years of this century account for some of the lack of interest.

Grover Plate Number
348 Vase, 7", cased blue cut to silvered crystal, signed.   250

Other Examples
1. Goblet, 6", silvered glass cased in green, Revi p194   175
2. Pitcher, 7", silvered and vintage engraved, Revi p195   350

SILVER DEPOSIT

This particular technique is sometimes called Silver Overlay or Silver Inlay. Since it is actually a deposit of metallic silver on glass by electro-deposition Silver Deposit seems the most descriptive of the three and is therefore used in this book. The silver is applied in the same way that silver plated metal articles are produced with one exception. When applied to glass it was used as a decorative pattern and not an over all coating.

In order to do this the glass object was coated with a conductive material in the areas where silver was desired. In the electroplating bath the silver would only be deposited on the coated areas. Fine examples of this work are found on small boudoir bottles and colognes, sometimes on crystal and infrequently on ruby, cranberry, or green. A limited amount was done on Steuben Verre de Soie by the Alvin Silver Company. Any of these command a real premium over an undecorated piece.

Silver Deposit

1. Bottle, cologne, 4", silver & monogram on crystal. Illus.   40
2. Bottle, dresser, 5", silver on gr. Verre de Soie, signed   175
3. Center Piece, black satin glass, Tiffin (?).   30
4. Pitcher, 6", heavy silver w/cupid on crystal, Revi, p199.   150
5. Pitcher, lemonade, crystal, & six tumblers.   140
6. Vase, 6", scrolls in silver on green glass.   80
7. Vase, 4½", green overlay.   35
8. Vase, 5½", green overlay.   170

SILVERIA GLASS

The name given by Steven & Williams to a double-walled glass having a sheet of silver foil between the two layers. In this manner the foil was kept from blackening as it was completely trapped between the two layers so that air could not reach it. With the foil thus embedded an unusually attractive decorative effect was attained. Whether or not any other firms in Europe or America made this same type of glass has not been recorded. The Stevens & Williams pieces may carry their mark in the form of the joined initials "SW".

425

Grover Plate Numbers
342 Vase, 11½", bottle shaped, good condition.   420
343 Vase, 9", pinched sides, signed SW.   460

Other Examples
1. Bowl, oval, green vine & cranberry bottom.   200
2. Vase, 15", stick, below average example, unsigned.   140
3. Vase, 7", bulbous, foil appears tarnished, unsigned.   110
4. Vase, 10", gourd shape, not signed.   160
5. Vase, 11½", signed S & W.   500

SINCLAIRE GLASS

Glass by this name was made in Corning, New York, by Henry P. Sinclaire Company. Some of their pieces are marked with an "S" in a wreath. Because some of their pieces are identical in shape and color to known Steuben pieces, collectors have considered the "S" as a Steuben signature. The exact story is yet to be uncovered but since Mr. Sinclaire was once a director of the Hawkes company which was a co-founder of Steuben, there is a good possibility that they may have purchased wares from Steuben and added their own signature. This seems likely as their principal product was fine cut glass made from blanks

150

1. Bowl, engraved grape & vine design in two colors.   250
2. Candlesticks, pr, 10", crystal, vintage engrav., sgn'd S.   pr 200
3. Centerpiece, 10", on ped., black w/white edge, sgn'd S.   180
4. Clock, 8", mantle, copper wheel engr., sgn'd, Illus.   250
5. Compote, 7", black glossy glass w/ivrene edge, sgn'd S.   125
6. Plate, 12", cut class in garlands & stars, signed S.   240

SMITH BROTHERS GLASS

A decorating firm in New Bedford, Massachusetts, that originally did decorating as part of the Mt. Washington Glass Company of that city. Some of their work is signed with a standing lion in a shield. The high quality of the enamelling makes these sought-after pieces. Even the decoration may be very similar to some designs by Mt. Washington due to copying of popular designs by one or the other. Some artists are known to have been employed at different times by each shop.

325

known to have been employed at different times by each shop.

Grover Plate Numbers
114 Vase, 9", cylindrical w/colored bird, signed.	150
115 Vase, 8½", floral mum design, signed.	400
116 Vase, 8½", flask shaped, Santa Maria design, signed.	325

Other Examples
1. Bowl, rose, tan, decorated w/daiseys.	150
2. Box, powder, 4"D, melon rib, decorated.	175
3. Jar, mustard, scenic design, unsigned	110
4. Jar, biscuit, 7", silver top, floral design, signed.	220
5. Vase, 10", floral decoration, signed.	250

SPANGLE GLASS

A glass using small flakes of mica or similar materials to produce a decorative effect. This was done by taking the first gather of glass and rolling it in the shiny flakes that had been sparsely scattered on the table. This first gather of glass was then cased with a clear or amber crystal to seal in the flakes and produce a smooth finished surface. A similar technique was used with different particles to produce Spatter, Aventurine, and Vasa Murrhina Glasses. Spangle glass was made both here and abroad. Since pieces are usually unsigned, it is difficult to attribute the work to a given factory. This type still in production.

100

Grover Plate Numbers
398 Pitcher, creamer, 5", silver on blue. Illus.	100
399 Basket, 8", rainbow, crystal overlay and feet.	350

Other Examples
1. Tumbler, water, 4", silver on cobalt blue.	30
2. Vase, 7", gold spangled design on rose background.	65

SPATTER GLASS

Any article using multi-colored pieces of glass to produce a decorative effect. This was done by taking the first gather of glass and rolling it in small pieces of glass that had been sprinkled on a table. The gather may then have been reheated and reworked to blend the particles into the main body. Finally a casing of clear glass was added to produce a smooth glassy surface finish. See Spangle and Adventurine for descriptions of very similar wares which are sometimes con-

40

Spatter Glass

fused with Spatter. A very similar glass, if not identical, was termed End-Of-Day based on the story that gaffers at the end of the day were permitted to use up small odd lots of colored glass to make up pieces for their own disposition. If so, they would more likely resemble a marbled glass from mixing several small lots of hot glass together. More on this under the heading End-Of-Day.

Grover Plate Numbers
400 Jar, 6", covered, predominating brown coloring.   80
403 Vase, $10\frac{1}{2}$", bottle shape, blues & purples, signed.   125

Other Examples
 1. Basket, small, bronze dore holder.   60
 2. Basket, 8", spatter w/white lining, clear thorn handle.   50
 3. Bowl, card receiver, w/oval mirror in dore mount. W-p23   275
 4. Bowl, 10", spatter coloring, pleated top.   60
 5. Bowl, bride's, 10", rainbow spatter, crimped edge.   135
 6. Candlesticks, pr., 8", spatter on blue background.   65
 7. Lamps, oil, fonts in red & wh. spatter, applied decor.   pr. 450
 8. Pitcher, water, 8", multi-color spatter on blue.   75
 9. Sugar shaker, 5", silver top, spatter on rose background.   25
10. Shoe, miniature, 3", high type, good colored spatter.   15
11. Toothpick, blue spatter.   20
12. Toothpick, $2\frac{1}{2}$", fine spatter on red background.   35
13. Tumbler, water, 4", spatter, almost marbled.   30
14. Vase, pr. 7", varigated colors.   pr. 40
15. Vase, 6", pink and white speckled.   30
16. Vase, 7", end of day flaired, speckled.   30
17. Vase, 6", gold spatter yellow incased glass.   25

STAR HOLLY GLASS

Actually a milk glass product and would normally be classified as such but like Holly Amber and a few other pressed glassed items, it has attained a higher stature because of scarcity coupled with high demand. This is listed here principally because it is included in ART GLASS NOUVEAU by the Grovers. Made by Imperial Glass Company c. 1900 as an imitation of the Wedgewood jasper dinnerware from England. The backgrounds are colored in the Wedgewood jasper colors in a flat finish, while the holly leaf borders are left in the basic glossy milk glass.

100

Grover Plate Numbers
407 Bowl, 9", Rosso Antico (brick) color, signed "IG". Illus.   100
408 Bowl, sugar & underplate, blue jasper, signed "IG".   140
409 Goblet, water, 6", green jasper, signed "IG".   80

Other Examples
 1. Creamer, red & white border, Imperial.   55
 2. Spooner, blue border in holly pattern, Imperial.   45
 3. Tumbler, water, $3\frac{1}{2}$", green holly edge. Imperial.   50

ILLUSTRATIONS OF STEUBEN GLASS

ACID CUT BACK 1200	AURENE 350	CALCITE 3500	CINTRA 1000
CLUTHRA 900	CRYSTAL 900	DIATRETA 9000	FLORENTIA 3000
INTARSIA 2800	IVORY 550	IVRENE 675	JADE, YELLOW 2800
MOSS AGATE 2500	ROUGE FLAMBEE 3200 each	VERRE DE SOIE 325	TYRIAN 3000

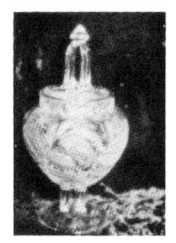

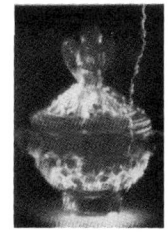

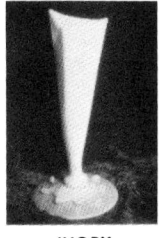

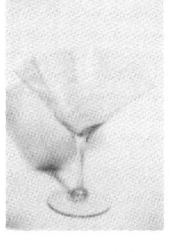

STEUBEN GLASS

With reference to Art Glass, this name embraces the many types of decorative and utilitarian glass made by the Steuben Glass Company from the time it was founded in 1903 by Frederick Carder and Thomas Hawkes in Corning, New York, until 1918 when it became the Steuben Division of the Corning Glass Company. It also embraces the production of colored and clear crystal by the Steuben Division from 1919 to 1933 while Mr. Carder was Art Director. From 1933 to 1953 Mr. Carder worked in semi-retirement in his laboratory at the Steuben Division and turned out a very limited number of pieces in unusual and unique glass formulations. These later pieces are also included as Steuben Glass. Therefore, Steuben Glass really represents any glass produced under the direction, design, or influence of Frederick Carder. As such, a more accurate and descriptive term would be Carder Glass which some day it should be rightfully called.

In 1933 a drastic re-organization resulted in the discontinuing of colored glass production. A new management dedicated to the use of only the extremely fine clear crystal glass in decorative and tableware items used designs created by Sydney Waugh and later artists. In the thirty-four years that have followed, this same policy has been rigidly maintained. The only exception has occurred in the last couple of years when the precious metals of gold, platinum and silver have been combined in some of the very limited production of fine art pieces and paperweights. This later Steuben Glass (since 1933) in its finer forms is also appearing in shows and sales as very desirable item of collectible Art Glas. It therefore seems logical at this time to divide Steuben Glass into two broad categories or sub-divisions. First, Carder Steuben Glass (or Carder Glass). This group includes anything produced by or under the direction of Frederick Carder. The second group includes anything that has been produced by the Steuben Division of the Corning Glass Company from 1933 to the present date and called late Steuben or Steuben Division Glass to distinguish it as something separate and distinct from that produced during the colored glass era. Examples of Late Steuben are included in the following list because of the increasing interest in the finer pieces as they begin to appear in important collections throughout the country.

Carder Steuben Glass was produced in some twenty distinct classifications that are named and collected. It is impractical to give full details on each one here because of the space required. The following books give it all or in part. Grovers', ART CLASS NOUVEAU, Rockwell's, FREDERICK CARDER AND HIS STEUBEN GLASS. The listings given below are reference to Grovers' book. The prices of pieces illustrated in all other books are given in Hotchkiss' PRICE GUIDE TO FREDK. CARDER'S STEUBEN GLASS.

Gardner lists about one hundred and forty different colors used by Carder. He also itemizes about thirty special and standard techniques in manipulating and final finishing of glass articles at Steuben. About twenty of the better known classifications have been used in grouping the various examples described and priced in the following sections or classes. Space limitations preclude a full explanation of each type. For this information the following books are recommended. Gardner's recent, *The Glass of Frederick Carder* is the most authoritative and exhaustive book done on this subject. A smaller inexpensive complete book in full color is Rockwell's *Frederick Carder and His Glass*. As already mentioned Grovers', *Art Glass*

Steuben - cont'd

Nouveau contains about fifty color plates on Steuben alone. The author of this book has a pocket book in print entitled: *Carder's Steuben Glass Handbook and Price Guide* which contains basic information as well as prices for all of the illustrations in the above three books.

Acid Cut Backs
Grover Plate Numbers
281 Bowl, 4", blue aurene to alabaster, signed F. Carder.	1200
282 Vase, 12", black to alabaster, signed F. Carder.	1250
283 Vase, 11½", green to yellow jade.	900
284 Vase, 10", green to alabaster, signed F. Carder.	800
285 Vase, 14", blue jade, alabaster & black, signed.	2400

Other Examples
1. Vase, jade green & alabaster, 6"H. Rp18-A	675
2. Vase, black and alabaster, 8"H. Rp18-B	750
3. Vase, Rosaline and alabaster, 6"H. Rp18-C	750
4. Vase, blue aurene & yellow jade, 9"H. Rp18-D	2000
5. Vase, Rosaline, 12"H. Rp18-E	1000
6. Vase, gold aurene & black, 9"H. Rp18-F	2500
7. Vase, gold aurene & alabaster, 9"H. Rp18-G	1750
8. Vase, black & alabaster, 10"H. Rp18-H	1000
9. Vase, gold aurene & alabaster, 9"H. Rp18-I	1750
10. Vase, Rosaline, 12"H. Rp18-J	900
11. Vase, 3 color cluthra, 14"H. Rp18-K	1850
12. Vase, Rosaline & alabaster, 12"H. Rp18-L	900

Aurenes

Grover Plate Numbers
261a Bottle, perfume, 8", blue aurene, signed.	**240**
269 Vase, 10", blue aurene w/buttons, signed F. Carder.	**575**
270 Decanter, gold aurene, signed F. Carder.	**400**

Other Examples
1. Vase and holder, 4"H, gold aurene. Rp9A	250
2. Cordial, blue aurene, stemmed, 7"H, Rp9-B	240
3. Bottle, cologne, 8"H, blue aurene. Rp9-C	300
4. Basket, 5"H, handle, gold aurene. Rp9-D	475
5. Vase, 9"H, ribbed, blue aurene. Rp9-E	350
6. Vase, 9"H, 3 handles, gold aurene. Rp9-F	275
7. Vase, 10"H, panelled, blue aurene. Rp9-G	350
8. Compote, 9"H, stemmed, gold aurene. Rp9-H	200
9. Dish, salt, 2"H, gold aurene. Rp9-I	90
10. Vase, 9"H, 3 handles, blue aurene. Rp9-J	550
11. Dish, salt, 2"H, gold aurene. Rp9-K	100
12. Goblet, 8"H, Venetian, gold aurene. Rp9-L	200
13. Candlestick, 12"H, tulip, gold aurene. Rp9-M	275
14. Goblet, 6"H, twist stem, gold aurene. Rp9-N	180
15. Vase, 15"H, collar, gold aurene. Rp9-O	275
16. Wine, 6"H, twist stem, gold aurene. Rp9-P	160
17. Candlestick, 12"H. tulip, gold aurene. Rp9-Q	275

Steuben - cont'd..

Cintra

Grover Plate Numbers
279 Candlestick, 10", red & blue stripes, signed F. Carder	475
299 Vase, 8", bird design.	3750

Other Examples
1. Compote, 7", red & blue stripes, signed F. Carder.	1000

Cluthra

Grover Plate Numbers
278 Vase, 10", blue cluthra w/handles, signed F. Carder.	700

Other Examples
1. Vase, 8", fan, shaded blue to white, signed.	500
2. Vase, 5", yellow to white, not signed.	400
3. Vase, blue and white, 7"H. Rp22A	500
4. Vase, chartreuse, 7"H. Rp22-B	375
5. Vase, rose and white, 5"H, Rp22-C	350
6. Vase, rose mottle, 7"H. Rp22-D	700
7. Vase, blue and white, 8"H. Rp22-E	650
8. Vase, rose, 7"H. Rp22-F	600
9. Vase, yellow, 10"H. Rp22-G	400
10. Vase, black, 5 pipes, 12"H. Rp22-H	650
11. Compote, rose to white, 6"H. Rp22-I	550

Crystals, Colored and Clear

Grover Plate Numbers
293 Jar, covered, $8\frac{1}{2}$", black threaded, signed F. Carder.	240
294 Vase, 3 prong, 6", cerise ruby, signed F. Carder.	180
295a Bottles, cologne, 12", topaz.	140
295b Bottle, cologne, 12", celeste blue.	160
296 Decanter, 11", clear w/overlay of cherries.	300
297 Goblet, water, silenium red, engraved, signed.	175

Other Examples
1. Glass, pilsener, marina blue, signed. Rp16-A	125
2. Vase, 8", fan, D.Q, gold ruby, signed. Rp16-B	200
3. Bottle, perfume, 9", Rosa, signed. Rp16-C	175
4. Vase, 6", Bristol yellow, black threads, sgn'd. Rp16-D	100
5. Goblet, water, 7", antique gr., threaded, sgn'd. Rp 16-E	80
6. Compote, 7", celeste blue and Rosa, signed. Rp16-F	225
7. Goblet, water, $7\frac{1}{2}$", Pomona green, signed. Rp16-G	70
8. Goblet, selenium red, 8"H. Rp16-H	150
9. Candlestick, marina blue & amber, 10"H. Rp16-I	125
10. Bottle, Pomona green & amethyst, 10"H, Rp16-J	250
11. Vase, amethyst, 14"H. Rp16-K	350
12. Candlestick, Rosa & Pomona green, 12"H. Rp16-L	175
13. Bottle, perfume, celeste blue, 12"H. Rp16-M	300

Steuben - cont'd.

Decorated Aurenes

Grover Plate Numbers

259 Vase, 8½", decorated blue aurene, signed F. Carder.	700
262 Bowl, 3", red, signed F. Carder.	2400
263 Vase, 10", red, signed F. Carder.	3600
264 Vase, 8", brown, signed F. Carder.	3000
265 Bowl, 3", blue, signed.	1500
266 Bowl, 3", footed, green, signed.	1000
267 Vase, 7", green, signed F. Carder.	1150
268 Vase, 6", rose, signed F. Carder.	1800

Other Examples

1. Vase, 9"H, green, vines & leaves. Rp10-D	1250
2. Vase, 9"H, green & gold loops. Rp10-I	1600
3. Vase, 8"H, gold aurene, leaves. Rp10-K	700
4. Vase, 13"H, green, trumpet, feathers. Rp10-L	1200
5. Vase, 9"H, gold aurene, pulled, footed. Rp10-M	500
6. Vase, 8"H, gold, leaf, vine, millefiori. Rp11-B	900
7. Vase, 5"H, gold, leaf, vine, millefiori. Rp11-C	750
8. Vase, 9"H, red, leaf & vine. Rp11-D.	3200
9. Vase, 9"H, green, leaf & vine. Rp11-F	1500
10. Vase, 9"H, red, pulled, gold & white. Rp11-L	3500
11. Vase, 9"H, green pulled feathers. Rp12-D	1800
12. Vase, 9"H, gold chain band. Rp12-F	3000
13. Vase, 8"H, gold aurene, leaves & vines. Rp12-M	2000

Diatreta

Only a few pieces of this rare glass were made relatively late in Mr. Carder's long life. Rarely is one offered for sale as they are treasured possessions of family and museum. The only one known to be offered recently was priced well into the five figured numbers.

Grover Plate Numbers

290 Vase, 6", varigated shades of amethyst, floral.	10,000
291 Vase, 8", varigated shades of blue/greens, figures.	9000

Other Examples

1. Vase, 7½", acid finish crystal in geometric design. Rp30A	8000

Florentia (Rear Cover #33)

Another of Mr. Carder's late creations of which it has been reported that less than a dozen were made by him. A soft appearing acid crystal is inset with pastel leaves at the bottom which creates the illusion of an unrecorded flower form. See Grover #307, Rockwell Plate #20, and Whitlow Page #37. If and when any of the pieces appear on the market they may be two thousand dollars or over as they are a extremely rare reminder of Carder's genius in art and technology.

Grover Plate Numbers

307 Vase, 7", green leaves in satin finish surface.	2800

Other Examples **Florentia**
1. Candlestick, 5", salmon leaves in satin surface. Rp26-A 1600
2. Compote, 6"D, salmon leaves in satin surf. Rp26-B 3000
3. Tazza, 6", green petals in satin finish. W-p37. 3600

Intarsia
Inlaid in blue, black, or cerise ruby between two layers of clear crystal in floral or random pattern. Intarisa is another art form attributed solely to Carder. In some cases the bowls carry his name in script on the lower part

Grover Plate Numbers
298 Vase, 6", footed, blue floral. 2700

Other Examples
1. Bowl, blue leaf design, 4"H, Rp22-C 2750
2. Vase, blue leaf design, footed, 10"H. Rp22-D 3250
3. Bowl, black maze, 4"H. Rp22-E 3000
4. Goblet, lavender daisy, 8"H. Rp22-F 2000
5. Vase, black, daisy design, 7"H. Rp22-G 4000
6. Goblet, black varigated, 8"H. Rp22-H 2000

Ivory

Grover Plate Numbers
280 Vase, 12", lily shape in opaque white irides., sgn'd. 650

Other Examples
1. Candlestick, 4", petal top, white irides. Rp24-G 180
2. Vase, 14", urn shape, handled, white irides. Rp24-H 750
3. Vase, 12", scalloped top, white irides. Rp24-I 500

Iverene

Grover Plate Numbers
286 Vase, 10", creamy white opaque, black foot, signed. 275

Other Examples
1. Fruit, pear, 3", creamy white & leaf, unsigned. Rp24-A 200
2. Vase, 5", creamy white, unsigned. Rp24-B 200
3. Vase, 5", Rp24-C 300
4. Vase, 8". Rp24-D 275
5. Animal, elephant on base, $3\frac{1}{2}$"H, unsigned. Rp24-E 375

Jades

Grover Plate Numbers
261b Bottle, perfume, 8", long stopper, Rosaline signed. 250
261c Bottle, perfume, 8", long stopper, blue jade, signed. 350
271 Bottle, cologne, $5\frac{1}{2}$", yellow jade, signed. 350
272 Vase, $5\frac{1}{2}$", yellow jade & applied Blue Aurene decor. 1000
273 Vase, 7", blue jade w/feather decoration. 1800
274 Compote, $8\frac{1}{2}$", footed, blue w/wh. trim, signed Carder. 850
275 Vase, 14", green prong, alabaster foot, signed. 275
276 Vase, 12", dark blue jade, signed Carder. 650
277 Vase, 12", Rosaline cut to alabaster, signed A.C.B. 900

Other Examples   **Jades**
1. Perfume, blue jade, alabaster stopper, 8"H. Rp20-A   400
2. Bowl, yellow jade, 4"H. Rp20-B   375
3. Perfume, blue jade, alabaster stopper., 8"H. Rp20-C   400
4. Vase, jade green & alabaster, 10"H. Rp20-D   150
5. Bowl, jade green & alabaster, 10"H. Rp20-E   225
6. Pitcher, jade green & alabaster, 10"H. Rp20-F   250
7. Vase, Rosaline & alabaster. 10"H. Rp20-G   300
8. Vase, alabaster, 10"H. Rp20-H   350
9. Basket, Rosaline & alabaster, 10"H. Rp20-I   425
10. Candlestick, blue jade & alabaster, 10"H, Rp20-J   400
11. Compote, blue jade & alabaster, 10"H. Rp20-K   900
12. Candlestick, blue jade & alabaster, 12"H. Rp20-L   400
13. Sugar, Rosaline & alabaster, 4"H. Rp21-A   190
14. Vase, Rosaline & alabaster, 8"H. Rp21-B   400
15. Creamer, Rosaline & alabaster, 4"H. Rp21-C   200
16. Perfume, jade yellow, 10"H. Rp21-D   350
17. Vase, dark blue jade, 7"H. Rp21-E   750
18. Perfume, jade yellow, 7"H. Rp21-F   350
19. Basket, lt. blue jade, 7"H, Rp21-G   800
20. Vase, blue jade, 9"H. Rp21-H   650
21. Vase, blue jade, 8"H. Rp21-I   600
22. Candlestick, green jade & alabaster, 11"H. Rp21-J   160
23. Bowl, amethyst jade, 9"H. Rp21-K   900
24. Candlestick, green jade & alabaster, 11"H. Rp21-L   160

Moss Agate
A stone type glass made by Carder in a mixture of opaque rich reds, browns, and green.
Grover Plate Numbers
300 Vase, 12", rich brown & yellow, signed F. Carder.   2500

Other Examples
1. Shade, lamp, 7", unsigned. Rp25-G   750
2. Vase, 7", dark browns & greens, unsigned. Rp25-I   2400

Oriental Poppy
A Steuben type that has some resemblance to Pastel Tiffany in its colors and faint stripes. Somewhat denser and of heavier construction. Not common and may be confused with other wares unless signed, documented, or an exclusive Steuben shape, such as the characteristic twisted stem used in candlesticks and compotes. The value approximates some of the better known Cluthras.
1. Vase, rose & opalescent, stripes. R26-F   900
2. Compote, rose & opalescent, 7"H, stripes. R26-G   750
3. Vase, 7", blue & opalescent, rib. R26-H   800

Rosaline
Belonging to the Steuben jade family that might well have been named Rose Jade. Milky rose color often found with a trim or foot of alabaster. An appealing and desirable addition to any collection. See the Jades for examples and comparisons with other jade colors.

Rouge Flambee

Another of the little-seen type of Steuben Glass but remembered once seen for its striking rich red tomato color in a dense opaque body which Mr. Carder reported as extremely difficult to make and likely to be unstable structurally. The few pieces that are seen are almost without exception in important collections and therefore, like similar rarities, values can be an approximation of what a seller and buyer might agree upon. The scale of value would place it above Intarsia and below Diatreta.

Grover Plate Numbers
302 Plate, $8\frac{1}{2}$", plain rimmed plate, signed.   1800
303 Vase, $4\frac{1}{2}$", deep tomato w/silver leaf/vine decor.   5200

Other Examples
1. Bowl, 5", deep tomato in flattened sphere. Rp26-A   3600

Verre de Soie

A particular favorite of Mr. Carder who used it extensively, in fact so much so that it has probably tended to depress its current values well below their true worth and importance. Found in many beautiful decorative forms and with additional decorations. It was also used widely in tableware and table pieces in quite simple styles. Also known by its English translation of Silk Glass which it truly resembles because of it semi-transparent iridescence, especially when displayed against a dark background.

Grover Plate Numbers
292 Decanter, 8", white iridescent w/green stopper.   275

Other Examples
1. Vase, fan, 12"H. Rp24-K   300
2. Compote, fruited finial, 6"H. Rp24-L   275
3. Vase, handles, 10"H. Rp24-M   225
4. Shaker, 8"H. Rp24-N.   250
5. Jar, covered, fruited finial, 12"H. Rp24-O   450

Tyrian

Not one of Carder's most beautiful creations but certainly belonging in the class of his rarities because so few pieces were made. This is thought to be less than a dozen or so. It is found with the name Tyrian signed in the lower part of the body of vases. It is a green-blue body with silver, gold leaves and vines worked into the surface. In the value scale any piece that is representative would fall in with Intarsia and Florentia

Grover Plate Numbers
306 Vase, 10-1/4", blue/greens w/silver leaf & vine.   3000

Other Examples
1. Bowl, 4", blue/greens w/silver leaf & vine. Rp27-D   2800

Sculptured

Usually found in figural form, this glass is characterized by its frosted or matte appearance and rough surface texture. Made from original sculptures by Mr. Carder by two methods, Cire Perdue, (lost wax casting process in which the original was destroyed in casting) and by casting (pressing) for simple figures and bas-relief. Obviously the values range greatly for this very rare classification with the single Cire Perdue figures commanding prices around the mid five-figure numbers. The plaques of well-known

Sculptured (Cont'd.)

persons like Edison and Lincoln produced in some unknown quantities would be worth only about one tenth to one fifth as much as of the one-of-a-kind pieces.

Grover Plate Numbers
289 Candlestick, Heltmet figure in matte finish.　　　　　　　2500

Other Examples
1. Statue, 15", Grecian male, matte finish. Rp29-A　　　　　5500
2. Plaque, horses cast in matte finish, 10". Rp29-B　　　　　600

Steuben - cont'd

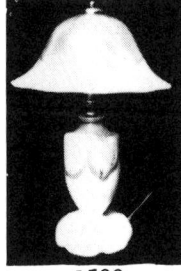

Lamps and Shades

As this fourth edition goes to press lamps of the Art Nouveau and later period are much in demand with collectors and decorators as evidenced by the high prices and some reproductions.

One of the rarest items in Steuben is a complete two piece table lamp in decorated Aurenes or Calcite. Mr. Carder's original sketch books show some fifty designs dating from around 1910 to 1932. All of them appear to be table lamps ranging from small boudoir lamps 10" high to about 24" for the higher table varieties.

1500

While lamps are a Steuben rarity, the small shades used originally for gas lights and later for electric ones are probably the most available items of Steuben. There were about 500 different designs (shapes) plus numerous variations is the decorating or finishing available over the years. What a challenge this presents to the shade collector. And Steuben was only one of the suppliers. Most of these had the standard 2¼" opening at the top where it was held to the fixture by three screws. There are some very rare items among this assortment. The brown Aurene with zig-zag band, the Decorated Aurene, and Calcite with blue leaf and vine are three of these.

It has been reported that Steuben dominated the field during the first quarter of the century in shades and bowls.

All of the original designs from Mr. Carder's sketch books of the above items are reproduced with their original numbers in Gardner's book, *The Glass of Frederick Carder*.

Darrah Roberts is just out with another new book on *Art Glass Shades* which covers many of the Steuben items plus those of other manufacturers such as Durand, and Tiffany, all in full color.

1. Lamp & shade, 17", calcite/gold & gr. feathers, #2335.　　1500
2. Lamp, 12", threaded blue aurene shaft in metal mount.　　500
3. Lamp Base, 15", ACB black to Cintra.　　　　　　　　　　1200
4. Lamp, reading, 50", with 12" brown aurene shade.　　　　750
5. Lamp, boudoir candle holder & shade in gold & green.　　300
6. Lamp, boudoir, decorated gold aurene #584.　　　　　　　600

STEUBEN DIVISION GLASS

This term is being used for the production of the Steuben Division of the Corning Glass Company from 1933 to date. From the years of the Great Depression, this division concentrated on the production of the highest grade clear lead crystal. For thirty-four years the only deviation from that policy has been adding some accents in silver and gold in recent years. Never once during this period of time have they produced any colored glass. Much of this fine crystal started out as additions to discriminating collections, both private and museum. Many of the pieces are unique and were made for presentation to heads of state and other noted persons. Fortunately, the production of this Division has been well documented by company catalogues and catalogues of special exhibitions. This fine brilliant crystal was sometimes further enhanced by copper wheel engraving after designs by outstanding artists.

700 pair

The first such designer who worked for Houghton in this new assignment was Sidney Waugh. One of his designs in pure crystal was the Trigger Fish listed below, a pair of which are in the Toledo Museum in Toledo, Ohio.

A collector's series that was very popular is the Audubon plates. Each plate in crystal was engraved with one of the birds from the famous Audubon Book. A massive Gazelle Bowl designed by Waugh with a band of engraved gazelles in full flight is in the Metropolitan Museum. This animal was also used by Carder in some of his structural and artistic glass. A smaller chalice-like vase with a single gazelle signed "Steuben 1935" is listed below. In addition to the fine decorative pieces, Steuben Crystal was also used as tableware items. To fully appreciate the design and quality of this crystal requires proper lighting and dark backgrounds, without which much of its appears undistinguished, especially the smaller pieces such as candlesticks. Steuben Crystal has always sold at a premium price even for common items as tableware. The finer pieces are priced from several hundred to several thousand dollars. All work is signed Steuben in very fine script using a diamond point.

1. Ashtray, 5", crystal w/single rest, signed Steuben.   40
2. Bowl, 9", ribbed crystal, signed Steuben.   150
3. Bowl, 6", blocks of cut lines, signed Steuben, c. 1936.   75
4. Candlesticks, pair, 4", tear drop crystal, signed Steuben.   100
5. Figure, Trigger Fish, pair, 10", by S. Waugh, Illustrated.   700
6. Figure, "Whale, Nantucket", Houston, limited edition.   3500
7. Goblet, 5", tear drop stem crystal, signed Steuben.   30
8. Plate, 10", engraved Audubon Eagle, signed Steuben.   350
9. Vase, 8", engraved by Waugh, signed Steuben 1935.   300

STEVENS & WILLIAMS GLASS

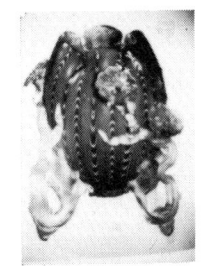

375

One of the great glass companies still in existence in the Stourbridge area of England. What today is classed as Art Glass probably originated with the work that John Northwood did for them in the last quarter of the 19th century in the famous hand carved masterpieces of Cameo Glass like the Portland Vase. Some of these took four years to complete. From this beginning the firm has produced many different types of Art Glass such as Overlay, MOP, or Satin Glass. It was at this plant that Frederick Carder worked from 1880 until 1902 when he came to America to start the Steuben Glass Company. For this reason some of their production bears a resemblance in either shape or color to Steuben. One example is Rosaline. It is very difficult to attribute any particular piece of Art Glass to Steven & Williams unless the piece bears their initials "S&W" or is documented in some other way. See *European Art Glass*, by Ray and Lee Grover for more information and examples.

1. Bowl, rose, MOP, crimped, chartreuse liner. 495
2. Bowl, sugar, sterling cover & handles, decor., 5". 40
3. Bowl, small, 4"D, Rosaline. 100
4. Ewer, 8", gourd shaped, pull-up pattern. 390
5. Pitcher, amber w/blue handle, tear drop, 9". 350
6. Sherbet, Rosaline & alabaster, signed S & W. 120
7. Vase, air trap, butterscotch swirl. W-p17. 250
8. Vase, blue, 8", cluthra type (S&W?). 75
9. Vase, blue glass curved, rose decor., signed S & W. 350
10. Vase, 4", English Cameo, floral w/butterfly, signed S&W. 250

SULPHIDE GLASS

180

Not really a type of glass but rather a type of decoration used in glass. Usually a flat piece of porcelain in bisque form embedded in a piece of glass. The bisque piece previously having been molded to form a relief portrait or figure. Most frequently found in old paperweights and also new limited editions. This form of decoration was also used by Bakewell in other pieces, such as the bottom of tumblers about 1815 and later in animal form in large crystal glass marbles. For more information see the particular classification as mentioned here.

ILLUSTRATIONS OF TIFFANY GLASS

AGATE 1600	CAMEO 1800	DIATRETA 3200	FLOWER FORM 650
INTAGLIO 400	LAVA 3600	LAMP 2750	MILLEFIORE 3000
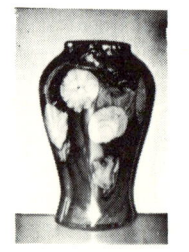	PAPERWEIGHT 4000	Pastel 375	
10,000	3100	4500	4250

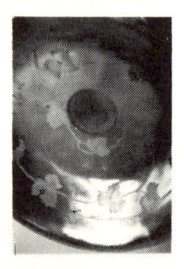

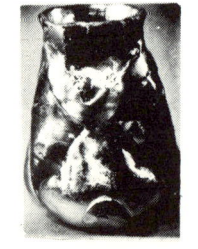

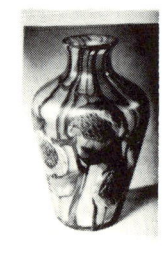

TIFFANY GLASS

For one hundred and forty years the name of Tiffany has stood for the highest quality in jewelry, silverware, and fine decorative home accessories. A member of the family, Louis Comfort Tiffany, established the family name on an equally high plane in the field of glassware, both decorative and tableware. He first made an international reputation in creating beautiful works of art in stained glass before developing his now world famous Favrile Glass about 1895 in the popular Art Nouveau style. He received valuable assistance in this venture from Arthur J. Nash, an accomplished glass expert from England. Not content with glass alone as a media, he also did unusual work in bronze in desk sets and lamp bases. He also designed and made some pottery decorative items in the same modern style.

Much of his glass was signed by carving the letters "L.C.T." or some combination of his given names and family name on the bottom of the pieces with an engraving tool. The signature was usually accompanied by a number or letter preceding a number. For example the words "A. Coll" preceding the number is supposed to indicate that this was a specially made piece. Paper labels with a monogram in Art Nouveau style were also used and account for some pieces not having any identification today.

Unlike his contemporaries, Tiffany's work does not always fall into well-defined classification. Two rather well-defined ones, however, are very well-known to collectors. These are his iridescent Peacock Blue and Gold Iridescent wares. He produced a great deal of tablewares, such as complete services of stemware in gold iridescent glass. Since very similar iridescent colors were used concurrently by Steuben, Durand, and others, unsigned pieces are sometimes difficult to tell unless the piece has a shape that is typical of one of the several factories.

Two very distinctive Tiffany products were Lava and Cypriote glass. These were designed to represent respectively volcanic action and the actions of the elements on ancient glass. Production of these types was so limited that today they are high-priced rarities.

Some of his decorative pieces and occasionally his tableware were further embellished by engraving designs in them by the copper wheel method. This work is generally referred to as Tiffany Intaglio. He also produced some Cameo pieces in which the background was removed by acid or cutting which left the design in relief. Some of these are shown in Grover's book on page 110 and have a slight resemblance to French Cameo. Many collectors consider his Paperweight glass as his finest creation. These are frequently floral designs introduced between two layers of glass. He also used pieces of Millefiore set into the surface of other colorful vases. And, of course, some of the rarest pieces combine one or more of the above techniques.

Listed below are pieces that range from very small cabinet pieces in bronze which sell for a very nominal price up to rare one-of-a-kind pieces valued in the thousands. The monumental punch bowl made for, the Paris Exhibition in 1900 and illustrated in the second edition of Koch's book. *Louis Comfort Tiffany,* is probably worth at least ten thousand dollars today. Prices depend on rarity, demand, colors, and artistic merit of a given piece and as a result may vary greatly among time, place, and person.

Agate Glass
A marbelized type of glass in very limited quantities to represent natural stone formations and striations.

Grover Plate Numbers
167 Decanter, 9", wine, brown agate, vert. white lines, sgn'd.	500
202 Vase, 5", brown and yellow agate, signed.	1600
203 Vase, 8½", brown & tan agate, signed.	3000
204 Vase, 6", yellow w/black double circles, signed.	2400
205 Vase, 10", laminated brown & tan stripes, signed.	1800
206 Vase, 5", marbleized brick color, signed.	1750

Cypriote Glass
A realistic representation of ancient buried glass with similar eroded and roughened surface in iridescent finish.

Grover Plate Numbers
191 Vase, 7½", gold cypriote, signed Louis C. Tiffany.	1250
192 Vase, 9½", brown iridescent, signed.	1500
193 Vase, 7", blue iridescent Cypriote, signed.	2000
194 Vase, 7½", decorated black iridescent Cypriote, signed.	2500
195 Vase, 7", amethyst paperweight Cypriote, signed.	3250

Favrile Glass
The word "Favrile" is so closely associated with Tiffany's work and signatures that an explanation of the term is in order. According to authorities, this term was derived from an archaic word that meant hand made, having the same root as the word "fabricate." Accompanying the signature or label it indicated that this was a hand made piece as most of his work was. Therefore this is not a class or type of Tiffany, rather it refers to the general method of producing it.

Floriform Glass
A very popular form of Tiffany vase. A long thin stem rising from a rather standard foot was surmounted with an almost infinite variety of floral forms and colors. Even though they were produced in abundance they are in great demand and represent excellent examples of Art Nouveau in shape and coloration.

Grover Plate Numbers
140 Vase, 13½", flower-form, green & white, signed.	575
141 Vase, 13", flower-form, tulip shaped, wh. & gold, sgn'd.	650
142 Vase, 13", flower-form, elongated body, fine design, sgn'd.	750
143 Vase, 19", gold irides., Jack-in-Pulpit, signed.	360
144 Vase, 14", flower-form, red & blue, flat top, signed.	850
145 Vase, 14", flower-form, Gr. &wh. cameo deocr., signed.	2000
146 Vase, 18", flower-form, pink cameo decor. bronze base.	1400
147 Vase, 18", flower-form, green & white, signed.	675
148 Vase, 14", flower-form, jack shape, gold decor.	725

Other Examples
1. Vase, gold irides., tulip shaped, w/long stem & ped. base.	550
2. Vase, stick, 10", irides. blue w/feather design, sgn'd LCT.	375
3. Vase, tulip shape, pearl w/green leaf design, sgn'd LCT.	500

Intaglio and Cameo Glass

Intaglio usually refers to glass that is incised by copper wheel engraving which is the case for some Tiffany pieces. Other examples of his work were also produced by acid etching, commonly called Acid Cut Back or ACB. These are termed Cameo to distinguish from the other techniques and have been combined together here for convenience.

Grover Plate Numbers
207 Vase, 4", paperweight, floral, cameo & intaglio, sgn'd.   2900
208 Vase, 6", red cameo cut to yellow, signed.   2800
209 Vase, 8", decorated floral cameo, signed.   1600
210 Vase, 8", irides. cameo, peacock in relief, signed.   2500
211 Bowl, $9\frac{1}{2}$", blue irides., vintage intaglio design, signed.   700
212 Vase, 7", intaglio floral in crystal, signed, T&C mono.   1500
213 Vase, 16", green irides., intaglio cut, narcissus des., sgnd.   700
214 Vase, $11\frac{1}{2}$", purple & green vintage, intaglio, signed.   1750
215 Plate, 6", irides. peacock feather design, signed.   900
216 Vase, 7", paperweight, peacock feather design, signed.   3000
217 Tazza, 8", blue irides., diatreta cage on stem, signed.   3250

Iridescent and Decorated Glass

As with other contemporary producers of Art Glass more of this type of glass was made by Tiffany than any other. The fact that it was made as tableware alone accounts for voluminous production. The gold and blue iridescent colors predominated and in many cases are difficult for other than the expert to distinguish from Durand, Quezel, or Steuben.

The iridescent pieces that were decorated are much scarcer and command a good premium over an undecorated piece. Marvered heart and vine was frequently used as were various combinations of pulled threads, loops and feathers.

Grover Plate Numbers
148 Vase, $14\frac{1}{2}$", modified jack, decorated gold irides., sgn'd.   725
149 Vase, 11", irides. red with gold overlay, signed.   340
150 Vase, $8\frac{1}{2}$", brown irides., double threads, signed.   450
151 Vase, 10", brown irides., gourd shape, signed.   350
152 Vase, 9", iridescent, opalescent, gourd shape, sgn'd.   900
153 Vase, 11", brown iridescent w/floral decor., signed.   800
154 Vase, 6", blue iridescent, free form, signed.   560
155 Vase, $18\frac{1}{2}$", blue irides., decorated top, signed.   760
156 Vase, 8", green iridescent, black & green decor., sgn'd.   875
157 Chalice, 11", gold iridescent, green leaves, signed.   600
158 Vase, $8\frac{1}{2}$", green irides., scroll decoration, signed.   850
159 Vase, $4\frac{1}{2}$", red iridescent, high collar, signed.   1800
160 Vase, 9", red iridescent, decorated collar, signed.   3500
161 Vase, $5\frac{1}{2}$", red iridescent, decorated collar, sgn'd.   3600
162 Bottle, cologne, 8", black irides., scroll decor., sgn'd.   1250
163 Vase, 13", blue irides., silver decor., good neck, sgn'd.   2000
164 Vase, $12\frac{1}{2}$", stick, red irides., signed.   2500
165 Vase, $8\frac{1}{2}$", blue satin, iridescent, signed.   1000
166 Vase, 6", blue satin, irides., vertical stripes, signed.   1200
168 Vase, $6\frac{1}{2}$", red & black irides., panels, signed.   2000

Iridescent and Decorated Iridescent (Tiffany)
Grover Plate Numbers

168 Vase, $6\frac{1}{2}$", red & black irides., panels signed.	2000
169 Vase, 4", blue irides., pinched & ribbed, signed.	450
170 Vase, 5", blue & black irides. decorated, signed.	875
171 Vase, 4", red irides., decor. w/silver, signed.	1500
201 Vase, $6\frac{1}{2}$", irides. lava, signed.	3100
202 Vase, 5", brown & yellow agate, signed.	2500
203 Vase, $8\frac{1}{2}$", brown and tan agate, signed.	3000
204 Vase, 6", yellow w/black double circles agate, signed.	2800

Other Examples

1. Bowl, blue irides. w/ruffled trim, signed LCT.	350
2. Bowl, finger, 3", gold irides., ruffled edge, signed.	140
3. Bowl, $3\frac{1}{2}$" D, footed, blue irides., fair color.	375
4. Bowl, footed, w/blue irides. border, LCT signed.	400
5. Bowl, 7", deep, golden iridescent.	210
6. Candlestick & shade, 13", fluted base, golden irides.	280
7. Candlestick, 8", gold iridescent, signed.	125
8. Compote, 11"H, gold irides., signed LCT.	450
9. Cordial, $1\frac{1}{2}$", gold iridescent, signed.	100
10. Cup, loving, gold irides., 3 handled w/leaf & vine design.	750
11. Cup, vintage punch, gold irides., LCT Favrile.	265
12. Dish, candy, gold irides., signed LCT.	250
13. Dish, individual salt, gold iridescent, signed.	80
14. Goblet, 10", golden iridescent & green stem.	300
15. Plate, under, bluish gold irides., signed LCT Favrile	125
16. Salt, blue iridescent, signed.	140
17. Sherbet, gold iridescent.	170
18. Tumbler, juice, irides., reeded decor., signed LCT.	100
19. Tumbler, water, 4", gold iridescent, intaglio, signed.	190
20. Tumbler, water, 4", gold iridescent, pinch-sided, sgn'd.	140
21. Tumbler, juice, gold irides., lily pad patt, unsigned.	150
22. Vase, 6", red iridescent, slight imperfection, signed.	1750
23. Vase, 6", footed, blue iridescent, signed.	360
24. Vase, 10", trumpet shape, blue iridescent, signed.	450
25. Vase, 10", stick shape, blue iridescent, signed.	350
26. Vase, green iridescent, silver decor., signed LCT.	550
27. Vase, bud, 6", gold iridescent, hexagonal.	175
28. Vase, 8", stick shape, blue irides., wide bottom, sgn'd.	350
29. Vase, stick, blue iridescent, wide bottom, signed 1115.	335
30. Vase, gold iridescent, draped & pinched. Signed #7294H.	250
31. Vase, 19", stick, blue irides., bronze support, signed.	375
32. Vases, pair, blue iridescent, signed LCT Favrile. pr.	750

Lamps and Lighting

No other category of Tiffany's output has experienced the overwhelming demand that the fabulous lamps produced in so many styles and colors his direction have. Originally these were high priced articles made to exacting standards of workmanship and design. Bedroom, desk, table and floor as well as hanging types were a few of the many styles that originally

Tiffany Lamps

ranged in price from about fifty dollars to five hundred. Because of the wide spread interest in all lamps of this period and particularly in Tiffany, we have tried to show and list as many examples as possible. All are signed. Several books are available which give more information. Of special merit are *Louis C. Tiffany's Glass - Bronzes - Lamps* by Robert Koch and the extraordinary and expensive full color book, *The Lamps of Tiffany* by Dr. Neustadt, a collector's item in its own right.

Grover Plate Numbers
218 Table, 23", daffodil design shade, signed.	3500
219 Table, 17", Moorish mosaic shade, signed.	2500
220 Table, 20", shaded green bell shaped shade, signed.	1000
221 Table, 19½", lily base, 12 decor. lily shades, signed.	2750
222 Table, 29", apple blossom design shade, signed.	5000
223 Table, 29", dragon fly border, jeweled, signed.	4500
224 Table, 22", spider web, apple blossom design, signed.	6700
225 Table, 13", portrait, globular, blue irides., signed.	500
226 Table, 11½", mushroom shape, agate base, signed.	750
227 Candlestick, bronze & irides., gold balls, signed.	275
228 Table, 28½", deep wisteria, excellent color, signed.	10,000

Other Examples
1. Student, 14½", green, etched shade & bronze stand.	450
2. Oil, 15½", gold lustre in 3 parts, each signed.	600
3. Candlestick, 2, w/iridescent shades, signed. pr.	250
4. Drape pattern, glass shade, bronze ped. base, signed.	575
5. Melon shape drop, opal. gold, leaf decor., signed LCT.	375
6. Floor, decorated iridescent shade, signed LCT Favrile.	600
7. Table, dragon fly, jeweled, bronze base, signed.	4800
8. Desk, swivel green striped shade, signed.	320
9. Table, bronze base, 3 lily shades, signed.	800
10. Floor, 24", geometric shade, bronze base, signed.	2500
11. Table, 23", wide woodbine des., border in rose/yellow.	4000
12. Table, 23", Sexahedron pierced bronze shade.	350
13. Chandelier, 27"D, flat dome, wisteria design.	1300
14. Chandelier, 21"D, geometric dome, leaf border.	1300
15. Student, double, 12", gold ruff. iridescent shades.	425
16. Entrance, 18", six inverted urn, gold irides. shades.	1200
17. Table, 22", geometric dome w/Greek key border.	1500
18. Table, 27", arrowroot leaves/blossoms.	4250
19. Table, 21", seven lily gold irides. shades.	2100
20. Table, 20", white apple blossom dome, green leaves.	1600
21. Mantle, 13", two 3-lily shade lamps, gold irides. pr.	1500
22. Shade, 14"D, decorated gold & green iridescent.	500
23. Table, 30", conical shade w/pink fruit.	1200
24. Student, 14", calcite type shade in "U" mount.	250
25. Floor, base only, tree style, 70".	1000
26. Table, 27", conical shade in marbled tan geometric.	1300
27. Chandelier, 24"D, iris blossom design in pink & blue.	1650
28. Shade, lily shape in gold iridescent.	180
29. Shade, 6", gold iridescent, bell shape.	35

Lava Glass
Usually in free form with body color overcoated with irregular bands or stripes of contrasting color giving the impression of flowing molten glass.

Grover Plate Numbers
196 Vase, 6½", banded iridescent lava, signed. 3600
197 Vase, 4½", decorated lava. 2250
198 Vase, 5", decorated irides. lava, peacock feather, sgn'd. 2000
199 Vase, 5", iridescent banded lava, signed. 3400
200 Vase, 6½", iridescent lava, beaded decoration, signed. 3250
201 Vase, 6½", iridescent lava, signed. 3100

Millefiore Glass
Small millefiore (thousand flowers) wafer florets are used sparingly to enhance the floral decoration on iridescent glass. These are imbedded in the surface of the glass while hot.

Grover Plate Numbers
172 Vase, 5", gold iridescent w/millefiore decor., signed. 1000
173 Vase, 7½", greenish irides., millefiore & leaves, signed. 950
174 Vase, 11", white irides., millefiore & gold leaves, signed. 1200

Paperweight Glass
A very special technique of implanting colored glass in the form of complete flowers between two layers of crystal or contrasting colored glass. The spectacular results achieved in very limited quantities have made any example a prized possession.

Grover Plate Numbers
175 Vase, 7", marbled paperweight, signed. 1000
176 Vase, 8", nasturtium paperweight, signed. 2400
177 Vase, 8", morning-glory paperweight, signed. 4000
178 Vase, 12", gladioli paperweight, signed. 3200
179 Vase, 4", narcissus paperweight, signed. 2400
180 Vase, 5", marine scene paperweight, signed. 2100
181 Vase, 5", marine scene paperweight, crystal, signed. 3000
182 Vase, 14", red flower paperweight, signed. 2750
183 Vase, 12", aquamarine paperweight, signed. 3500
184 Vase, 4½", crocus paperweight in crystal, signed. 3250
185 Vase, 8", red paperweight leaves & vines, signed. 4000
186 Vase, 16½", blue floral paperweight, metal base, signed. 4500
187 Vase, 6½", red crocus paperweight in crystal, signed. 3000
188 Vase, 7", narcissus paperweight in gold irides., signed. 2100
189 Vase, 5½", floral paperweight, gold irides. liner, signed. 2750
190 Vase, 8", poppy paperweight, signed. 3000

Pastel Glass
A combination of attractive light colored crystals combined with a very light milky opalescence concentrated near the top edge are given the broad name of Pastel Tiffany. These pastel articles were produced in both table and decorative items in quantities so limited that they are now high priced compared to the same article in the same color crystal without the opalescence.

Pastel

Grover Plate Numbers
137 Vase, 7", pastel blue, signed LCT.	425
138 Vase, 6", yellow pastel in crystal base, signed.	240
139 Tazza, 7", pink pastel base and bowl, crystal stem. sgn'd.	550

Other Examples
1. Bowl, 12", footed, yellow & opal., signed.	370
2. Bowl, miniature, 2", pastel rose, signed.	240
3. Bowl, centerpiece, 12", blue opalescent, signed.	500
4. Compote, 7", pastel, imperfect.	125
5. Goblet, rose pastel feathered, signed.	200
6. Goblet, 9", long stemmed, light green pastel, signed.	300
7. Goblet, 6", pastel blue, signed.	250
8. Lamp shade, miniature in pastel, signed.	80
9. Parfait, green feathered pastel, signed.	175
10. Parfait, large green pastel, signed.	150
11. Parfait, small green pastel, signed.	165
12. Parfait, 5", footed, lavender & opalescent, signed.	200
13. Plate, pastel blue, signed.	160
14. Plate, 6", pastel, signed LCT Favrile.	150
15. Sherbet, green feathered pastel, signed.	185
16. Vase, pink pastel, trumpet shaped, engr.base, sgn'd 1896	375
17. Vase, lavender, jug-shape, pearl top & gold decor., sgn'd.	375
18. Wine, green pastel feathered, signed, label.	175

Tiffany Glass (Miscellaneous)

Vase, $13\frac{1}{2}$", blue iridescent, stick, enamel on copper base. sgn'd	325
Vase, gold irides., trumpet w/bronze base, signed LCT	275
Vase, 9", blue, silver swirl & swag decor., signed LCT.	950
Vase, stick, gold irides. green, feather patt., signed LCT2134M	500
Vase, bud, on cabinet base, pearl gold/irides. green, sgn'd.	450
Vase, bud, $6\frac{1}{2}$", irides.blue, green leaf & vine decor.	650
Vase, 15-3/4", bronze brown, paper label, vine & leaf decor.	450
Vase, 12-1/4", bud, gold irides., trumpet shape, signed LCT.	250
Vase, irides. gold, leaf & vine design, signed.	650
Vase, 7-3/4", Cypriote, blue, decor., platinum bronze.	950
Vase, $14\frac{1}{2}$", enameled, copper, repousse, corn stalks.	1600
Vase, 16", Floriform, signed LCT, 9708A.	375
Vase, Floriform, lobed bowl, ruffled rim, green leaves.	400
Vase, Floriform, upright petals, white to red-gold.	385
Vase, baluster shaped, cameo cut, blue, signed.	1050
Vase, 10", ovoid, translucent, iridescent blue.	500
Vase, 6", bulbous, red, silvery zig-zags, signed.	1650
Vase, 12", flower, green & white irides., blue highlights.	525
Vase, Floriform, gold & green, signed LCT Favrile.	350
Vase, 14", paperweight, lily pads.	1800
Window, stained glass, river landscape.	1350

Bronzes, Enamels and Pottery (Tiffany)

275

In addition to the Tiffany Furnaces the company also operated a metal fabricating shop and a pottery. Of course many of the bronze castings were lamp parts for the leaded and iridescent shades made of glass. In addition to these articles many all bronze items were made as desk sets, ashtrays, and other accessories. In many cases these were combined with small pieces of colored glass to further the decorative appeal. Many bronze candlesticks were made in this manner.

The enameling was usually done on copper and some very artistic pieces were made in the form of vases, boxes and trays. These items were heavily embossed overlaid with thin sheets of silver or gold and then enamel glazed to produce deep iridescent sheens in complementary colors. Such items are scarcer than either glass or pottery items made by Tiffany. Any specimen warrants a very high price in today's market. The small 3½" enamel on copper vase illustrated at the left is an example. It is marked L.C.T. S.G. 73.

Pottery items made by Tiffany are scare and unusual in design and finish. Some appear at first to be metal because of the bronze glaze.

For further information on these categories plus an excellent dissertation, illustrations and price lists of lamps refer to *Louis C. Tiffany's Glass-Bronzes-Lamps* by Robert Koch.

1. Box, 4½", bronze glazed ceramic, signed LCT.	175
2. Candlestick, double, bronze, w/irides. studs top & base.	195
3. Calendar, desk, bronze mounted, Tiffany Studios.	40
4. Holder, desk pad, bronze, signed, Tiffany Studios.	25
5. Holders, candlestick, pr., '9", bronze & green. pr.	200
6. Inkwell, 6", solid bronze, yellow marble base, sgn'd.	100
7. Lamp, ceramic glazed decor., 3 handles, signed LCT.	325
8. Salt dip, enamel on copper.	275
9. Set, desk, 7 piece, mother-of-pearl insert.	225
10. Vase, 14½", ceramic, art nouveau, pompeian green color.	275

TORTOISE SHELL GLASS

Glass articles having the appearance of tortoise shell brown and yellow mottling and made of a double layer of glass with the brown colored particles in between them. Currently it is popular to attribute this glass along with many other types to the Boston & Sandwich Co. Like so many other attributions, it may be right with respect to a given piece and it may not. It is known that this glass was also made in Europe and it is not known how many factories made it. Examples are generally unsigned.

Grover Plate Numbers

130 Bowl, 4½", deep colors & iridescent.	125
131 Pitcher, 13½", amber handle.	155

Other Examples

1. Bowl, finger and plate, 3", good coloring, Revi p237	225
2. Box, dresser, 3", good mottle.	50
3. Set, tray & two jars w/covers.	175
4. Toothpick, 2½", widely spaced mottling.	45
5. Tumbler, water, 4", brown & yellow mottle, slight irides.	90
6. Vase, 8", narrow waisted & flared top, good coloring.	175

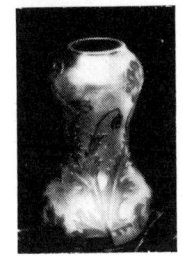

VAL ST. LAMBERT

Product of a factory by this name still producing glass in Belgium. This firm produced cameo glass contemporary with and similar to Gallé and Daum-Nancy of France, and any signed piece of this type would bring a price about the same as a piece of French Cameo of the same quality. See this classification for shapes, styles, and prices. They also produced glass similar to the French Lalique and still do. In this matte finish glass Val St. Lambert prices are usually somewhat less than a comparable piece of Lalique. They are also well known for their fine tableware which is still being produced. In this field the product is of a similar type to that of the French firm of Baccarat, but again would bring a somewhat lower price. This lower price is not necessarily due to inferior quality, but because it is less well known.

250

Grover Plate Number
370 Vase, $16\frac{1}{2}$", cameo and enameling.   400

Other Examples

1. Bowl, crystal overlay, blue rims, engraved, signed.   60
2. Tumbler, pink crystal, signed.   50
3. Tumble-Up, rare cameo. Tumbler & plate, sgn'd., cranb.   300
4. Vase, 10", double gourd in lavender flowers. Illus.   250
5. Vase, 8", French Cameo carving on cranberry red.   175

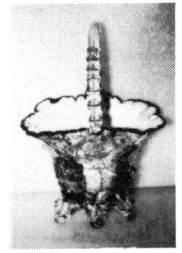

VASA MURRHINA GLASS

This name is usually applied to a piece of internally decorated glassware that has at least two different types of particles forming the decoration. Most frequently these are small pieces of colored glass and small particles of silver, gold or mica dust. Another way is saying that these pieces are often a combination of Spatter and Aventurine techniques. These materials were placed on the marver (work table) and rolled into the hot glass while it was being formed. Since this method is still being used in Murano, Italy after hundreds of years it is quite likely that this ware has been made in a number of countries and companies. From fragments excavated at the site of the Cape Cod Glass Company it is known that this type of article was produced during the years 1858 and 1882. The moderate prices for this type are perhaps due to inability to document its place and time of manufacture.

300

1. Basket, 10", white w/red and gold flecks.   90
2. Bowl, rose, 5", blue w/yellow and silver inbedded.   45
3. Pitcher, water, bulbous, brown & red with gold.   150
4. Pitcher, cream, cranberry w/white and silver specks.   45
5. Spooner, 5", ruffled top, deep red. Gold dust and yellow.   50
6. Toothpick, 2", yellow w/red and silver particles.   50
7. Tumbler, water, cranberry w/white and gold spatter.   35
8. Vase, 8", trumpet, dark red w/white and silver.   75
9. Vase, 6", bulbous, white w/amber/gold specks.   65

VENETIAN GLASS

Any glassfare that is made in the style popularly attributed to the Venetians such as millefiore or filigree decoration is now called by this name. It also refers to glass articles which follow the Venetian style of very light weight soda glass in delicate designs and added rigaree decoration. While the Venetians copied their millefiore from the ancient Egyptians and Phoencians, the rest of the world copied it from the Venetians who have dominated the world of glass since the Fourteenth Century. And interestingly enough they are still using some of the same techniques and designs in the pieces they produce on the island of Murano near Venice, Italy.

80

Grover Plate Numbers

379 Vase, 8", millefiore floral & net design c. 1805.	325
380 Pitcher, cream, 4", in large red clover design.	150
381 Vase, 8", vertical bands of millefiore and handles.	150
382 Vase, 8", floral millefiore and red lines on blue ground.	300

Other Examples

1. Bottle, 9", cranberry with enamel decoration.	50
2. Candlestick, Bohemia type w/hand painted decor.	35
3. Compote, 6", flat, white and gold decor. on green.	60
4. Cup & saucer, tea, blue & white twist filigree.	50
5. Dish, 8", dessert, Latticino in white and red.	85
6. Figures, birds, pair 10", shaded ruby to clear, 20th C.	75
7. Goblet, water, 9", high stem Latticino white design.	90
8. Lamp, miniature, 8", mushroom millefiore shade & base.	125
9. Paperweight, millefiore, dull, dome shape, modern.	20
10. Tumbler, water, 4", millefiore in shades of purple.	30
11. Vase, 8", in red & white filigree, handles, c. 1890. Illus.	80
12. Wine, 4", fine diam. w/encrusted gold band.	35

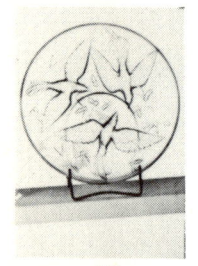

VERLYS

Principally known for molded (sculptured type relief design) pieces in a rather luminescent crystal with matte surface in the shape of bowls, figures, and vases. It is sometimes mistaken for Lalique even though the older Lalique work had a pronounced bluish opalescent tinge. This has been made in both the United States and France where it originated. A new small book on the company and its products will help in better identifying this collectible glass.

60

1. Bowl, 10", embossed birds in satin crystal.	60
2. Bowl, centerpiece 14", shallow with figures.	125
3. Bowl, 8", sculptured floral design in matte finish.	55
4. Plate, 12", heavily embossed, camphor finish, fish.	85
5. Vase, 6", cicade pattern in frosted glass. Illus.	50
6. Vase, 9", birds in trees in a matte finish crystal.	100

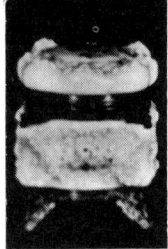

WAVECREST GLASS

One of three similar products of the C. F. Monroe Company of Meridan, Connecticut, that are identified by fine enamelled designs on an opal base. These pieces are usually in the form of boudoir accessories, such as powder boxes with gilded metal trim. The other named products are Nakara and Welva. Many of these pieces were signed with one of these three names. The prices and types are very similar. For more examples refer to listings under the other two names.

175

Grover Plate Numbers
110 Box, cover w/clock, blue, footed. 225
112 Jar, 4½", powder, fish design. 125

Other Examples
1. Box, jewelry, hand painted decor., 7". 150
2. Box, jewel, hinged lid, hand painted enamel flowers. 100
3. Box, 5", square, and cover, enamel panels in blue. 145
4. Box, puffed glass 6", in heavy colored beaded enamels. 175
5. Box, 4", banner mark. Tan and red decoration. 95
6. Bowl, sugar, silver lid & handle, enamel decor. 100
7. Humidor, cigar, panelled and enameled. Hinge cover. 125
8. Humidor, 5", marked "Cigars", gilt bands. 185
9. Jar, cracker, 6", silver top & handle. Scrolled enamel. 150

WEBB, THOMAS

Products of one of the most famous glass houses in England that operated under the name Thomas Webb & Sons in Stourbridge. Usually this name is used in conjunction with one of the other classifications of Art Glass to identify the source of manufacture or a characteristic variation of the art class. This applies to Webb Burmese, Webb Peachblow, Webb Cameo and many others. Some of their finest work was done in the beautiful hand carved cameo pieces in the 1880's. For further details with examples and prices, refer to the type of glass of which they were one of the sources. For more information and color illustrations see Grovers' *European Art Glass*.

375

1. Bottle, perfume, citron, flower & vine decor. 350
2. Bottle, 3-color citron, flower & vine decor. 375
3. Dish, salt, red. 300
4. Jar, rose water, frosted lemon yellow, signed, W-p31. 550
5. Pitcher, red to white. W-p18. 250
6. Vase, melon rib. Fishscale & vine decor., sgn'd. W-p18. 1350
7. Vase, blue miniature, flower & butterfly decor. 360
8. Vase, 3", w/white fuschias carved on red, impf. 65
9. Vases, table, pr., red to pale rose, 6½", W-p31. pr. 325
10. Vase, 6½"H. peachblow. 300
11. Vase, amber, cattails & butterflies, signed, 8½". 225
12. Vase, amethyst cameo glass, signed, 10", impf. on base. 200
13. Vase, 14", decorated. 125

REPRODUCTIONS, REPLICAS AND REISSUES

Reproductions of important types of glass have been made for centuries. Both Josiah Wedgwood and John Northwood of England made copies of what is today conceded to be one of the most important artifacts ever discovered, the Barberini or Portland vase. This beautiful, impressive black and white cameo vase was thought to have been made in Rome sometime in the first century. It was discovered in a tomb in Rome in the sixteenth century and remained in the Barberini for two centuries. It was then acquired by the Duchess of Portland. After it was loaned to the museum it was damaged but has been expertly restored.

In the Eighteenth Century Wedgwood reproduced this in black basalt with applied white figures. In the second half of the nineteenth century John Northwood reproduced it in glass by using a black glass blank which was cased with a coating of opaque white glass. He then hand carved the original design by carving away the white glass from the background and leaving the figures in shaded white relief.

Many other examples of reproductions of important articles of glass have been made available over the years. The famous Chinese Peachblow vase purchased by a Mrs. Morgan for the unheard of sum of some fifteen thousand dollars was reproduced by the New England Glass Company and the Wheeling Glass Company. These later pieces are now known as Morgan vases because of their distinctive shape and base.

Some of the replicas have been sponsored by well known and very prestigious institutions. The original motives behind such efforts were entirely noble and honorable. They were produced to make it possible for a larger segment of the public to acquire replicas of rare museum pieces for enjoyment in their homes at a very reasonable price. Of course this procedure is still being carried out by museums and art shops.

In most cases these replicas or reissues were suitably marked or at least easily distinguishable by size, color or other characteristics from the originals. They were offered for what they were and that is as a reasonable facsimile of the real thing. This is very commendable. Unfortunately several things have happened. Some of these replicas have found their way into the hands of unscrupulous dealers who have offered them as old and original items. They are usually priced well below current market prices as bait but far above their actual cost and true value.

In addition to this source of reproductions there have sprung up other sources that give the impression that they also have the public interest at heart by making replicas available to the public at lower prices. Actually these would be better termed forgeries as they are made to resemble the original as closely as it is possible to do and carry no identification to indicate they are copies. In fact if the original carried some type of markers identification on the bottom very likely these forgeries will have identical ones. While currently these are sold at normal mark-ups in gift shops, they are also heavily promoted through antique magazines. What the dealers do or charge for them is of no concern to the producers. One distributor of Art Glass reproductions is located in St. Louis.

At present a bill has been offered in both houses of Congress which is aimed at minimizing the possibility of people being deceived by such forgeries or reproductions. This bill provides for all glass being imported into the United States to be marked in some distinctive manner so that it is identifiable as to origin and date. Unfortunately this is still in committee and likely to remain there until the collecting public gets behind it and demands some action. After all the glass manufacturers are not anxious to go to all this trouble and expense, especially if it may narrow the potential buyers as such a bill might well do.

Until the time reproductions are under better control it behooves the collector to beware of such items being offered for something they are really not. The list of such items is extensive and it would be impractical to try to list all of them in this book as they are constantly changing. A few examples will illustrate the problem though. Today Mary Gregory glass is being mass produced in both Venice and Czechoslovakia. While a great deal of this is sold through normal gift shop distributing channels there seems to be little doubt that much of it is being offered as old. Mother of Pearl satin glass is another category where good reproductions are being offered in flea markets and other collectors' sales. Burmese, both the plain and decorated types, have been seen recently in a large Eastern antique market. Many contemporary paperweights that resemble old ones have strayed from their intended gift and department store outlets into shows, sales and auctions. These are much less likely to confuse the beginning collector than the many replicas of Victorian glass that seem to have been made for the sole purpose of finding a market for them in the antique trade.

At present the best solution for the problem of buying only genuine articles is to deal solely with highly reputable and knowledgeable dealers that are willing to guarantee the authenticity of everything they sell. In this connection there are many dealers that are perfectly honest but just don't know that they are selling something that is not what they think it is. This is why it is important to emphasize the contacts with experienced and informed dealers. Almost without exception any of these sources will gladly refund your money if it is later proven that your purchase was not as represented. This applies to those fine dealers that do business by mail. If there is any doubt in your mind about the integrity and knowledge of the person with whom you are dealing it is probably better to pass up what at the moment may seem like a remarkable bargain. Some very astute buyers will insist that the bill of sale will contain a statement that their money will be refunded if the articles purchased are found to be other than as represented within thirty days of the purchase date. The reputable dealer is always glad to rectify an unintentional error.

In the past several years many reproductions of this glass in the Diamond Quilted design (and probably others) have been appearing in a great many Flea Markets and on occasion in some of the better shows. Much of this is originating from an importing house in St. Louis that handles numerous other reproductions of high priced glass, pottery, porcelain, and anything else that is in demand. Ostensibly this firm sells to the gift shop trade but they advertise extensively in magazines about antiques and hold regional shows to which antique dealers are invited to buy at wholesale.

Some of the reproductions are quite well done and have misled a lot of unsuspecting people. There are usually small differences between these pieces and the genuine ones made in the late 19th century. Once these are pointed out they are quite obvious. In general the thickness and general appearance is heavier. Some shapes are not typical, the manner in which stoppers are made, and handles attached are other subtle differences. Best advice is to get a written guarantee from your dealer, that the piece is old and a refund will be made if this is not so.

MUSEUMS — PIECES AND PRICES

They don't mix.

The remarks here apply generally to any items in a museum collection whether related to trinkets or works of art, and are mentioned here more as reminders rather than as new information. This emphasis seemed appropriate since the Corning Museum of Glass was kind enough to permit some of their extensive collection to be used for the cover illustrations.

Museums make it possible for all of us to study and appreciate the past. Most of them go beyond the call of duty in helping interested persons obtain authoritative information. There is only one type of information that they unanimously refrain from giving and that is the value of any piece in their collection or a similar one brought to them for authentication. This is an especially sound policy and has the full backing of understanding collectors. If they did otherwise they would be putting themselves in the position of omnipotent judge of values and attempting to dictate prices, which are usually determined by the law of supply and demand. Their staffs are specialists in obtaining and disseminating reliable information. Their concerns are generally far removed from what is today's price of pieces in the collection. The marketplace is where specialists in developing information on prices are to be found and not in museums.

Therefore, no museum has had any part in arriving at the current prices shown in this manual. The fact that a piece described here is similar to one in a museum does not mean that the museum piece has the same value by any stretch of the imagination. For one thing, there may be many subtle differences not apparent to the reader, such as color. As pointed out earlier, even identical pieces can have a tremendous range in price depending on the numerous variables that are present at the time a sale is consummated. The more important the piece, the greater the variability.

Assumptions that a definite relation may exist between the values here and the values that might be assigned by a museum or private collector for any of their pieces illustrated in this book would be erroneous. The prices shown later should not be construed as being for a museum or private collector's specimen. Rather, they are for similar pieces that are known to those contributing price information and may differ considerably in details.

One other comment on museums and private collections might be pertinent to the discussion of values. Each one strives to obtain the best possible examples of their specialty as knowledge, effort and funds will permit. Most such collections do consist of many outstanding pieces. One result is that a great many people tend to stand in awe of such impressiveness and consequently feel that each example is priceless or nearly so. Such is not always the case. Many museum collections do, and should, show a fairly representative gamut of examples. Even then there is the tendency for most of us to overassess values when displayed in a glass case. The same piece in a flea market could well go unnoticed, unappreciated, and underpriced. This "halo" effect also applies to pictures in books.

APPENDIX

This appended material has been produced in fine type in order to include information that would otherwise have had to be omitted.

GLASS LANGUAGE

Some of the terms commonly used by glassmakers and glass collectors are listed in alphabetical order with a brief definition or interpretation. For those that would like additional information on specific methods, materials, and meanings, there are a number of good books available, such as *American Glass* by McKearin.

Air-twist: A decorative effect in glassware produced by pulling and twisting a glob of glass which has uniform entrapped bubbles.

Anneal: The method used to cool glass very slowly until it reaches room temperature in order to eliminate the strains which would shatter it if cooled rapidly. The old batch method of doing this has been superseded by the modern continuous electric ovens (lehrs).

Batch: The results of loading silica (sand), limestone and other chemical ingredients into a ceramic lined furnace and heating the mixture until it becomes a white hot homogeneous mass.

Bench: A specially designed seat with two horizontal arms or rails. The blower, when seated at it, rests his blowpipe across these rails and by rolling it back and forth can rotate the gather of molten glass to keep it from sagging while he is performing the finishing operations.

Blowpipe: A hollow iron rod, four or more feet long, used to dip into the furnace and obtain a ball of molten glass from which the glassblower would form a bottle by blowing into the opposite end.

Blown Molded: The process of hand blowing a gather of glass into a metal mold to reproduce the shape or decoration of the inside of the mold.

Charge: The various ingredients which are mixed together to be "charged" into the melting furnace.

Casing: An additional layer of glass (usually of a different color) which is obtained by dipping the original gather into a second tank of hot glass forming a skin coating of a contrasting color. By cutting through the outer casing, very pleasing two-toned effects can be created.

Cullet: Random size pieces of discarded broken glass which are salvaged by remelting again in a furnace in fixed percentages to the regular raw materials.

Cutting: The use of stone grinding wheels to incise various decorative designs on the surface of glass objects. These are usually then polished to give the same glossy appearance as the original surface.

Dip Mold: A heavy piece of iron or steel open on the top side and recessed in the approximate shape of the finished piece. After the glassblower lowers the gob of glass on the end of the blowpipe into it, he blows, causing the glass mass to take the shape of the recess.

Enamel: The material used in various colors to paint decorative designs on glass objects, which, when fired will fuse with the glass to form a permanent design. Many barber bottles were decorated in this manner.

Engraving: A method of using various sizes of copper wheels mounted on an overhanging, rotating spindle. By dripping a solution of fine abrasive on the wheel, the surface of glass is incised with designs of extremely fine detail. The finished design, having a satin finish from the abrasive contrasts with the shiny glass surface to create an illusion of objects in space.

Etching: The operation of dipping glass articles into hydrofluoric acid to eat away any of the surface that is not protected by some resistant material such as asphaltum. In this manner almost any name, design, or outline, can be permanently created on the glass surface having a contrasting satin finish.

Fire Polishing: The operation of reheating finished glass articles to give them a high gloss and to minimize any tool or seam markings.

Flint Glass: A composition of glass which was composed of silica made from flint stone rather than silica sand. Sometimes used interchangeably for Lead Glass. Wide mouth vessels made of this glass have a pronounced bell tone ring when given a sharp blow on the open edge.

Free Blown: The use of a blowpipe by a glassblower to completely form an object with the aid of some hand tools, but without the use of molds or other constricting devices.

Gaffer: A journeyman glassblower that acts as the head of a team of workers referred to as a "shop," and who coordinates their efforts to swiftly accomplish all of the steps in making a glass article before the gather of glass cools. The size of the shop will vary depending on the number and complexity of the operations, the most exacting ones being done by the master craftsman, the gaffer.

Gather: A glob of hot glass which adheres to the end of a blowpipe when it is dipped into a tank of molten glass and slowly rotated.

Glory Hole: A small opening in the glass furnace to reintroduce glass on the end of a blowpipe in order to reheat it for forming or polishing.

Hand Blown: Any object made using the blowpipe as contrasted to a mechanically blown bottle or light bulb of today. In either case, molds may have been used to determine the final shape of the piece.

Lead Glass: A composition of glass containing a high percentage (24 to 40%) of a lead compound which gives a "bell tone" to finished work.

Lehr: The furnace used for slowly cooling (annealing) glass articles to remove stresses within the glass. Today they are long conveyorized electrically heated tunnels.

Lime Glass: Glass produced by using lime as a flux for making clear thin articles. Does not ring like lead glass.

Marvering: The operation of rolling a gather of glass while still soft on a flat surface to shape it to its final contours. Also used as a means of imbedding other glass pieces such as threads, mica, and similar powders into the surface of the glass, still warm enough to receive them.

Metal: The glasshouse term for the batch of glass when it is ready to use by the glassblowing team.

Mold: A concave or hollowed out device usually made of iron into which the gaffer lowers the gather on the end of his blowpipe before starting to blow. As the gather expands from blowing, it takes the form and surface pattern of the mold.

Opal Glass: A translucent, but semi opaque glass having a milky white appearance, and therefore, referred to more frequently as Milk Glass which was produced by adding supplementary pigments to the batch ingredients.

Overlay: Preferably this term is only used to describe objects that have

APPENDIX
Continued

LIST OF REFERENCE BOOKS ON GLASS

Title	Price
AMERICAN ART NOUVEAU GLASS—Revi. Color, 462 pages	$20.00
AMERICAN CUT & ENGRAVED GLASS—Revi. 495 pages	15.00
AMERICAN CUT GLASS, Vol I—Pearson. 201 pages	15.00
AMERICAN CUT GLASS, Vol II—Pearson. Some color, 190 pages	15.00
AMERICAN GLASS—McKearin. 635 pages	14.95
ART GLASS NOUVEAU—Grovers. All color, 231 pages	27.50
ART GLASS SHADES—Roberts. All color	3.50
BOHEMIAN ENGRAVED GLASS—Pestova. B&W, 132 pages	3.98
BOSTON & SANDWICH GLASS CO.—Lee. 80 pages	6.95
CAMBRIDGE GLASS BOOK—Bennett. 96 pages	7.50
CAMBRIDGE GLASS CO. CATALOGUE—Welker. 120 pages	6.95
CARDER'S STEUBEN GLASS MANUAL WITH PRICE GUIDE—Hotchkiss. 120 pages	3.95
COLLECTIBLE GLASS #1—Lagerberg. 207 Color illus.	5.25
COLLECTIBLE GLASS #2—Lagerberg. 389 Color illus.	4.95
COLLECTIBLE GLASS #3—DURAND GLASS—Lagerberg. 234 Color illus.	4.75
COLLECTIBLE GLASS #4—BRITISH GLASS—Lagerberg. 361 Color illus.	5.75
COLLECTORS HANDBOOK OF AMERICAN ART GLASS—Barrett. Color, 24 pages	4.95
CRUETS ONLY—Murray. All color	4.50
CUT & ENGRAVED GLASS—Daniels. B&W, 441 pages	13.95
CUT GLASS HANDBOOK & PRICE GUIDE—Hotchkiss. B&W, 128 pages	4.75
ERICKSON FREEHAND GLASS—Knower. Color, 33 pages	4.95
EUROPEAN CARVED AND ENGRAVED GLASS—Grover. All color, 241 pages	27.50
FENTON STORY OF GLASSMAKING—Linn. All color	1.95
FORTIES REVISITED VOL. I—Lafferty. 80 pages	4.50
FORTIES REVISITED VOL. II—Lafferty. 160 pages	5.50
FOSTORIA GLASS CATALOGUE—Lafferty. B&W, 73 pages	5.95
FOVAL GLASS—Lafferty. Some color	5.95
FREDERICK CARDER AND HIS STEUBEN GLASS—Rockwell. Color, 32 pages	3.00
FRENCH CAMEO GLASS—Blount. 160 pages	15.00
FRY INSIGHTS—Lafferty. B&W, 52 pages	7.95
THE GLASS OF FREDERICK CARDER—Gardner. Some color, 373 pages	20.00
GREENTOWN GLASS—Boyd. 305 Color illus.	6.50
IMPERIAL GLASS—Ross. Some color, 40 pages	5.95
KEENE AND STODDARD GLASS—Lome. All color, 40 pages	4.95
L.C.T., REBEL IN GLASS—Koch. Some color, 246 pages	8.50
LIBBEY GLASS CO.—CUT GLASS—Ant. & Hist. Gloss. 25 pages	6.95
NEW ENGLAND GLASS & GLASSMAKING—K. Wilson. 400 pages	15.00
NINETEENTH CENTURY GLASS—Revi. Some color, 301 pages	12.50
PHOENIX—Lafferty. Some color, 94 pages	7.50
PORTLAND GLASS—Swan. B&W, 106 pages	6.95
SANDWICH GLASS MUSEUM COLLECTION—Sandwich. Color, 40 pages	3.95
TIFFANY'S GLASS, BRONZES AND LAMPS—Koch. Some color, 256 pages	8.50
TIFFANY GLASS—Amaya. Limited color, B&W, 84 pages	4.50
TUMBLERS WITH A PAST—Simon, All color	5.00

pieces of glass added to the base piece while hot to enhance the decorative appeal. Such additions are frequently in the form of simulated leaves and flowers, usually in contrasting color to the parent object. Overlay is sometimes used to denote complete second coating of glass over the first one prior to further cutting operations. The accepted term for this is casing. Overlay is also used for the depositing of Silver on glass. A more descriptive term and generally preferred is Silver Deposit.

Pontil: A solid iron bar about four feet or more in length, slightly enlarged on one end. It resembles the hollow blowpipe. It is used to hold a piece after it has been removed from the blowpipe so the gaffer can perform the finishing operations on the neck. This transfer from blow pipe at the neck to the pontil rod on the bottom is accomplished by pushing the hot pontil rod against the bottom and then severing the neck from the blowpipe. Finally, the article is separated from the pontil by a sharp blow which leaves a rough circular spot on the bottom. In fine pieces like decanters, this is ground away by using a small spherical grinding wheel.

Pontil Scar: The mark left on the bottom of an article with no further smoothing operations after it is separated from the pontil rod by a sharp tap.

Punty: A term sometimes used in place of the word pontil.

Rigaree: Applied glass decoration usually in the form of narrow bands of glass that have been pinched to form a ripple effect.

Servitor: One of the shop team that assists the gaffer by gathering the molten glass from the furnace and preparing it for him. The carry-away boy is the last to place the bottle into the annealing oven.

Shop: The term applied to the entire crew that is responsible for producing complete glass articles. The gaffer (head man or glassblower) a gatherer, finisher, servitor and carry-away boy.

Sick Glass: Refers to vessels that appear cloudy on the inside and resist most attempts to restore the natural brilliant surface. This type of cloudy effect is due to the surface of the glass being attacked, causing chemical decomposition of the surface. If the surface can be reached, it may be ground away to restore the surface. Other types of cloudiness are usually due to a deposit caused by evaporation of the contents, which can be dissolved or abraded off by numerous normal cleaning methods.

Snap Ring: Several movable fingers attached, in the form of an open cage, to the end of a rod. When these are contracted, they grasp the body of an article when it is removed from the blowpipe. It resembles the device to remove electric bulbs from high places. This device simplified glassmaking by eliminating the pontil and resulting pontil scar.

Turn Mold: A specially designed mold which rotates the article in the mold while warm, removing any vertical seam marks. Used on many other glass articles to produce a fine, undistorted surface.

ABBREVIATIONS

Grovers' ART GLASS NOUVEAU	G
Grovers' EUROPEAN ART GLASS	G2
Gardner's THE GLASS OF FREDERICK CARDER	Gd
Revi's NINETEENTH CENTURY GLASS	R
Revi's AMERICAN ART NOUVEAU GLASS	R2
Whitlow's ART, COLORED, & CAMEO GLASS	W